W9-CFZ-145

Case Studies in Systems Analysis in a University Library

Edited by:

Barton R. Burkhalter

The Scarecrow Press, Inc.
Metuchen, N. J.   1968

Acknowledgements

Although the papers in this collection have been authored in every case by the engineers who performed the study, it is also true that in every case much of the credit for the ideas must go to the library staff members with whom we worked. Those who have contributed, some in small ways and some in very large ways indeed, are unfortunately too numerous to enumerate here. However, special thanks is due Frederick Wagman, Director of the University of Michigan Libraries, and Robert Muller, Associate Director, for their initial conception and continuing support and wisdom.

The selection and editing of articles was accomplished with the assistance of several individuals. Many hours and insights were contributed by M. Carl Drott, whose intellectual mark was made on all the papers, and not just those he co-authored. In a like manner, I owe a considerable debt to Ronald E. Beck, James J. Cook, and Meredith Spencer. Finally, I'm happy to acknowledge Dean H. Wilson, whose vision has provided much of the sustaining motivation to carry through with this project.

Table of Contents for Case Studies in
Systems Analysis at a University Library

Introduction

Case Studies in Systems Analysis in a University Library
by Barton R. Burkhalter and Robert Muller

The marriage between the University of Michigan Library and Community Systems Foundation seemed like a sensible step at the time. Too often, Library administration found it necessary to choose between alternate courses of action without having adequate information. In addition, overburdened department heads rarely found time to alter their systems substantially to accommodate demands on the library and their departments, let alone time to make these changes in a systematic manner which considered the impact on other departments and carefully weighed alternative solutions. As a consequence of this situation, the library administrators were considering ways of providing staff assistance to themselves and the department heads, so that alternate courses of action could be designed and properly evaluated.

At about this same time, in early spring of 1963, members of the Department of Industrial Engineering of the College of Engineering at the University of Michigan recognized the need for systems engineers in community service institutions as well as in industrial enterprises. Consequently, Community Systems Foundation was incorporated as a non-profit organization; its purpose was to bring technical talent to bear on the problems of other non-profit community-service organizations. One way of accomplishing this purpose was for the Foundation to hire and train outstanding graduate engineers and student engineers, and then put them to work in community institutions.

The match was clear: the library administration desired a staff which would perform a systems engineering function, and Community Systems Foundation could provide that staff along with continuing technical supervision. Financial arrangements were made, and the program initiated in the summer of 1963. At the time of

5

this writing, January 1967, the members of the program have produced approximately forty studies and are hard at work on more. The case studies in this volume describe twelve of the most interesting projects carried out during this time.

It is important, we think, to point out the conditions under which these studies were undertaken. The study conclusions are not necessarily to be regarded as generally applicable; they were aimed at the solution of specific problems. It is the approach taken that is interesting, i.e., the use of various systems analysis techniques. In order to understand how these techniques worked at the University of Michigan Library, it is, of course, necessary to know the context in which they operated.

In the first place, the University of Michigan Library is a large and complex institution as libraries go. It has a collection of over 3 million volumes, a home circulation of about one million volumes per year, approximately 540 salaried and hourly employees, and 29 branch outlets located for the most part in separate buildings. It is expanding in an attempt to keep pace with the demands placed on it by a growing, multi-purpose state university. The key point is that the studies were not done in a small library or under static conditions. Often, the problems encountered were in large part due to a changing situation; they were solved in a very localized way.

The program carries the label "Operations Research" and reports as a staff unit to the Associate Director of the Library. Over its first three and one-half years, the program has been headed by three different graduate engineers working in this capacity on a part-time basis. Working under the department head have been anywhere from two to five part-time student engineers. Annually, the time spent by the department has averaged two to two and one-half man-years.

You will note that the case studies do not illustrate the use of very sophisticated techniques, such as linear programming or advanced statistical techniques. Rather, they employ more conventional tools, such as work sampling and measurement, methods improvement, and breakeven cost analyses. In many of the cases, the study simply amounts to marshalling the various costs, so that a rational

6

decision can be made. This straight-forward approach is the out-
growth of the basic operating philosophy which, more than any other,
governs the program, namely, that the results of the analysis are
what counts and not the analysis itself. In other words, proposed
systems must be implemented to be successful. Thus, each study
has two phases: the first in which goals are identified, alternate
systems posed and evaluated, and a report prepared for administrative consideration and decision-making; and a second phase where the
engineer and department staff work together to implement the changes
agreed upon. The two phases are analagous to the preparation of a
blueprint and the construction of the building. The goal of each study,
then, is not to discover new uses of advanced techniques, but to
solve specific problems in the most efficient way.

    This results-oriented approach has led to complete involve-
ment of the various library department heads in the studies. This
involvement begins with the identification of a need by a department
head. The best way for a study to be initiated is for a department
to ask the administration for assistance from the Operations Research
staff. There were only a few exceptions to this procedure, involving
requests by the administration for specific fact-finding studies. Department heads are encouraged by the Associate Director to request
assistance both by having the cost of the study paid for from the
central administrative funds rather than from the department's budget and on an informal basis. Periodically, the Associate Director
responsible for the program and the head of the Operations Research
Department meet to evaluate the current projects and to assign prior-
ities to the various study requests that have been submitted.

    During the data-collection and system-design phase, the en-
gineer works closely with the respective department head and his
staff. Goals are stated, data-collection procedures designed, partial
findings reviewed, and final recommendations arrived at prior to the
written report. In some of the studies, particularly those involving
layout changes, a series of conferences occur in which staff from
the area concerned evaluate proposed layouts many times in the process of arriving at an acceptable one. Some of the difficulties encountered in the program can be traced to inadequate communication

7

between an engineer and the department head concerned. This reinforces the need for involvement of the department head. Close communication between the department head and engineer does not necessarily mean that they always agree on the best solution. In cases of conflict, the department head's view generally prevails, since he must live with the proposed system, unless other arrangements are made by the administration.

Once the library administration has made a decision to proceed with a proposed system-change, the engineer works with the department head during implementation. This phase usually works well since a department head rarely has time to attend to the details of such a change and the engineer has both the time and intimate knowledge of what is required during implementation. He is in a position to make minor modifications in the proposed system during implementation to account for elements left out of the original system design. Rarely is a system designed without minor flaws; it is important to recognize these omissions and make adaptations during implementation.

A successfully implemented system often leads to further communication between a department head and the engineers. As further system changes are required because demand changes or other day-to-day problems arise, the department head may seek out the engineers for advice on data-collection or analysis.

The case studies contained herein are essentially modifications of reports by the student engineers recommending systems changes to the library administration. As such they have certain shortcomings. They seldom contain a description of the implementation process or an evaluation of the system made several years after implementation. This collection of case studies contains nothing in the area of technical services, a significant shortcoming, simply because no important studies had been concluded in technical services at the time of this writing. Also, one naturally finds differences in the work of various authors--in their styles, level of detail, and insight. But we feel the collection does contain many examples of how some of the basic tools of systems analysis can be applied to a university library; examples which we hope can lead others to use and improve the techniques.

Memo on Effective Labor Costs

    Labor cost is an important factor in most of the studies. Multiplying the number of hours devoted to a task times the hourly wage rate of an employee is not an adequate means of obtaining the total labor cost for the task, because the hourly wage rate does not represent the real cost to the Library. The Library must pay taxes and fringe benefits of various types over and above direct wages. Furthermore, over an extended period of time any employee has fewer productive hours than paid hours. If a particular task accounts for 10% of an employee's productive hours, then it should also account for 10% of his total cost to the library.

    The following calculation provides two factors which, when multiplied by the annual salary of a salaried employee or the hourly wage of an hourly employee respectively, produce the effective hourly cost to the library for this labor. In other words, it gives the total annual cost divided by the number of productive hours per year.

I. Salaried Workers*

  A. Total Cost per Dollar of Salary

1. Salary	$ 1.00
2. Fringe benefits and taxes (FICA, etc.) = 12%	.12 Cost $
	1.12 Salary $

  B. Productive Hours Per Year

1. Hours per year (Gross = 52x40)	2,080.0
2. Two weeks vacation	-80.0
3. Twelve days sick leave	-96.0
4. Six holidays + one "floating" holiday	-56.0
Actual hours in library	1,848.0
5. Coffee breaks (15 min/4 hours worked)	-115.5
6. Personal time (3%)+ Fatigue (3%)+ Delay allowances (5%) = 11%	-203.3
Total annual productive hours =	1,529.2 Productive hours per year

9

C. Effective Hourly Cost Per Dollar of Annual Salary

$$= \frac{1.12 \ (\text{cost \$/salary \$})}{1,529.2 \ (\text{productive hours/year})} = .0007324$$

For example, suppose a full-time employee earned an annual salary of \$6,000. Then his effective hourly cost would be:

$$6,000 \ (\text{salary\$/year}) \times .0007324 \left(\frac{\text{cost \$. year}}{\text{salary \$. prod. hours}}\right) =$$

$$4.39 \left(\frac{\text{cost \$}}{\text{prod. hours}}\right)$$

*Note: The figures for salaried workers appy to clerical positions. Librarians receive 4 weeks of vacation and work 35 hours per week. Thus their effective hourly cost per dollar is .0009418

II. Hourly

A. Total Cost Per Dollar of Hourly Wage

1. Wage   1.00
2. (No fringe or taxes are paid for hourly employees)   –

$$\overline{1.00} \ \frac{\text{cost \$}}{\text{Wage \$}}$$

B. Average Productive Hours Per Hour Paid

1. Start with one hour paid   1.00
2. (No allowances are made for vacation, holidays, or sick time)   –
3. Coffee breaks (25% of time no break; 75% of time 15 min/4 hours)   –.05
4. Personal time (3%) + Fatigue (3%) + Delay Allowance (5%) = 11%   –.11

$$\overline{.84} \ \frac{\text{Prod. Hrs.}}{\text{Paid Hr.}}$$

C. Effective Hourly Cost per Dollar of Hourly Wage

$$= \frac{1.00 \ \text{cost \$/wage \$}}{.84 \ \frac{\text{productive hours}}{\text{paid hours}}} = 1.19$$

Thus, a part-time employee earning \$1.00 per hour would have an effective hourly cost of \$1.19.

An Analysis of Renewals, Overdues and Other Factors Influencing the Optimal Charge-Out Period
by B. R. Burkhalter and P. A. Race

Library administration asked, "Should the length of the two-week charge-out period for student book loans be changed?" Initially the question arose in response to increasing pressure on the circulation staff. Lengthening the charge-out period might reduce the time the staff must devote to activities such as processing overdues and renewals. On the other hand, a shortening of the charge-out period might lead to greater book availability for the patrons. The purpose of this study is to identify the factors affected by a change in the charge-out period which lead to a change in cost or patron service, and then to attempt to assess the relative degree of change so that a decision can be made as to the optimal charge-out period.

The problem proved difficult. The process of identifying the factors, quantifying their estimated impact under different charge-out periods, and relating them in a rational way began to stretch out over a considerable period of months. Moreover, it became apparent that methods improvements could be made in some of the sub-systems relating to the central question of the optimal charge-out question. Therefore, three sub-studies were sequentially prepared over a period of twelve months which provided interim data and recommended methods changes in some of the sub-systems. The first of these reports deals with the renewal process; the second analyzes the overdue book process; and the third attempts to relate the previously obtained information on costs to patron usage data.

The Renewal Process

It was decided that renewals and overdues were the two important cost factors to be considered, and that book availability was the important service factor to be considered. The study of the renewal process set out to determine two items:

1) the cost of processing a renewal
2) the total number of renewals under the current system

Systems Analysis in a University Library

The change in the number of renewals under different charge-out periods was to be considered in the third study.

The cost of processing a renewal theoretically can be broken into labor and materials cost. However, no additional materials are used in renewing a book, so labor is the only consideration. Three separate operations were observed in the processing of a renewal:

> Desk -   At the main desk the staff member takes the carbon copy of the charge slip from the patron, searches in the main circulation file for the original, dates both the carbon and the original, returns the carbon to the patron, clips off the notification tape at the top of the original and places the original in a box for further processing.

> Exit Control - The exit control clerk takes the originals from the box to his station at the exit where he sorts them and puts on the proper notification tape in his spare time.

> File - A staff member transports the originals from the exit control back to the circulation file where they are filed when the circulation staff is not servicing patrons.

The time taken to complete these three tasks was determined by a time study. The results, given in minutes-per-renewal, are presented in table A.

Table A

Minutes of Library Staff Time Used in the Various Operations to Renew a Book - Results of a Time Study - University of Michigan Library

Operation	Minutes per Renewal
Desk	0.72
Exit Control	0.24
File	0.12
Total Renewal Process	1.08 minutes = 0.018 hours

The effective hourly cost, computed according to the procedure described in Memo on Calculating Effective Labor Costs, for these tasks is $1.19 per hour. Therefore the cost per renewal

12

equals (.018 hours x $1.19 per hour) = $0.0214 per renewal. The total semester cost, based on the frequency of renewal documented below, comes to $292.97.

There were found to be 13,690 renewals in the sixteen week period spanning the fall semester of 1963. These data are presented in Table B. Not all charged-out items included as part of the 83,228 total circulation were eligible for renewal: regular faculty may keep books indefinitely without renewal and student one-day circulation is not eligible for renewal. Thus, only student 2-week and faculty 4-week circulation is eligible for renewal, a total of 51,594 charge-outs. Renewals represent 16% of total circulation

$$\frac{13,690}{83,224} = .16,$$

but they represent approximately 26% of the circulation eligible for renewal

$$\frac{13,690}{51,594} = .26$$

In order to obtain the ratio of renewed books to the total number of books charged-out and eligible for renewal, we must first subtract the second and third renewals from the renewal data. In that way we can compare the number of books renewed once or more to the number of books circulated and eligible for renewal. Further probing into the renewal data presented in Table B indicated that less than 1% of the renewals were for a second or third time; all the rest of the books were renewed for a single time only. Thus, approximately 26% of the charge-outs eligible for renewal are renewed.

Although the dollar cost of processing renewals over a semester is relatively small (approximately $300), the large number of renewals indicates high social cost to the patrons doing the renewing. The documentation of the large number of renewals was an important factor in the decision to begin a study of telephone renewals, and in the decision by the administration to switch to a three week charge-out period.

Overdue Notices

Sending out overdue notices certainly costs the library money

13

Table B

Circulation Data from the University of Michigan General Library

Week of Semester	Ending Date	Total Circulation	Not Eligible for Renewal		Eligible for Renewal		
			Regular Faculty	Student One-Day	Faculty 4-Week	Student 2-Week	Renewals
1	9-8-63	3,223	854	86	79	2,154	50
2	9-15-63	3,796	903	156	131	2,456	150
3	9-22-63	4,520	873	260	141	2,846	400
4	9-29-63	4,607	827	258	121	2,801	600
5	10-6-63	4,814	840	288	145	2,841	700
6	10-13-63	4,924	788	318	155	2,900	763
7	10-20-63	5,140	780	288	198	3,036	838
8	10-27-63	5,137	919	300	99	2,993	826
9	11-3-63	5,899	943	362	105	3,529	960
10	11-10-63	6,260	804	341	216	3,766	1,133
11	11-17-63	6,530	800	442	124	3,936	1,228
12	11-24-63	7,853	875	614	143	4,821	1,400
13	12-1-63	5,129	582	450	78	2,529	1,490
14	12-8-63	7,016	797	580	142	4,447	1,050
15	12-15-63	4,925	619	316	99	2,738	1,153
16	12-22-63	3,455	545	136	74	1,751	949
Totals		83,228	12,749	5,195	2,050	49,544	13,690

14

and changing the charge-out period would be likely to affect the number of overdue books. It might be argued that the fines collected from overdues balance out the cost of sending overdue notices so that a change in the number of overdues would have no financial impact, but at the University of Michigan fines go into the general University fund whereas the cost of processing overdues comes out of the Library budget, a situation which causes the Library to work for fewer overdues. Thus, the cost of sending overdue notices and the estimated change in the number of overdues caused by a change in the charge-out period were considered important.

In the process of determining the cost and volume of overdues, it became apparent that the existing overdue notification process could be improved. Therefore, a sub-study analyzing these improvements was made along with the gathering of the cost and volume data. The following results were produced:

Volume - 2881 overdue notices were sent during the fall semester of 1963. Of these, 1600 were first notices, 750 second notices, and 530 third notices.

Cost - Approximate cost of processing these notices was $515, or about $0.18 per notice.

Recommended
Improvements - Eliminate the third overdue notice and possibly the second. Make the overdue notices on the Xerox rather than the photo-copy machine. Wait ten days to two weeks before sending the relevant notice rather than one week. These changes should result in semester savings of between $132 and $243.

The total cost of sending overdue notices was obtained by determining the individual tasks performed in processing the overdues and the labor and material cost associated with each task, and then multiplying the cost by the frequency of each task over a semester. Through observation and questioning, the following sequence of tasks was obtained for processing an overdue.

Procedure for Processing Overdues

1. Twice a week, charge slips three or more days overdue are pulled from the main circulation file.

15

2. Each charge slip is checked against the carbon charge slips from returned books whose original charge slips were not found in the main circulation file. The carbons are in the "snag box".

3. If a matching slip is not found in the snag box, the charge slip is sent to the Stacks Section where a search is made for the book in the stacks. If the book is not found in the stacks, the slip is returned to circulation.

4. There the charge slip is dated, taped, and sorted.

5. Then the charge slip is sent to the Photoduplication Department where a single photo-copy of it is made, developed, cut, stuffed in an envelope, and mailed.

6. The original charge slip is returned to the Circulation Department where it is filed in the overdue file.

7. If, after one week, the book has not been returned, the charge slip is pulled from the overdue file, steps two through six are repeated, and on the charge slip in the overdue file it is noted that a second overdue notice has been sent.

8. If the book has not been returned and the charge slip has not been pulled from the overdue file within a week of the second notice, a third and final overdue notice is sent after repeating steps two through six.

9. If the book has not been returned by a week after the third notice was sent, the charge slip is gold-tabbed and sent to Photoduplication where a Xerox copy is made. The original is returned to the overdue file and the copy is referred to a circulation clerk for special action. This action depends on the situation.

The assignment of labor costs, material costs, and frequencies to each of these tasks was primarily a matter of collecting the pertinent data. However, in computing labor costs it is important to note that some of the tasks consist of one time element which depends on the number of overdue notices processed and another element (associated with transporting the notices from one point to another within the Library) which is independent of the number of notices. The costs associated with transporting the slips is fixed over the span of a semester, since periodic trips (for example, two

16

per week) are made during which all accumulated overdue charge slips are transported at once. Table C presents the data on the man-time to perform each of these fixed time elements over one semester.

Table C

Processing Overdues: Man-minutes for Periodically Performed Tasks Whose Times Are Independent of the Number of Overdues

Task	Description	Unit Time* in Minutes	Frequency	Total Time per Semester in Min.
3	Transport slips from Circulation to stacks and back	1.2	twice/week	36
5	Transport to Photo-duplication, set-up machine, prepare mailing materials	12.3	twice/week	369
6	Transport originals from Photo-duplication back to Circulation	1.2	twice/week	36
9	Transport slips from Circulation to Photo-duplication and back to special Circulation clerk	2.2	twice/week	66
	Total			507

*Times are based on three time-studies taken over a period of two weeks.

Man-times which are dependent on the number of overdues are presented in Table D. Note the unit time to identify overdues is different for the first notice (step #1) than for the second (step #8) and third (step #9) notices. This is due to the fact that it takes longer to pull slips from the main circulation file than from the small overdue file. Frequencies for each task are also given in Table D and used to produce total man-time for the variable labor over a semester. (The time for the tasks in Table D was assummed to be linearly dependent on the number of notices processed, an assumption based on intuition and informal observation. Although no effort was made to check this assumption statistically, neither was there strong evidence which suggested the contrary to the data collectors. In view of the relative insignificance of this aspect of study, this seemed sufficient.)

17

Table D

Processing Overdues: Man-minutes and Frequencies for Tasks Whose Time Varies Directly with the Number of Notices

Task	Description	Unit Time* in Minutes	Frequencies**				Total Time per Semester in Minutes
			First Notice	Second Notice	Third Notice	Total	
1	Pull charge slip from Circulation File	0.17	2100	0	0	2100	357
2	Search snag box	0.76	2100	1000	580	3680	2796
3	Send, search in stacks, return	1.71	1950	870	550	3370	5760
4	Date, tape, sort return	0.21	1650	775	530	2955	620
5	Photo-duplicate, cut, stuff, mail	0.33	1600	750	530	2880	950
6	Return slip, file in overdue file	0.10	1600	750	530	2880	288
7	Pull from overdue file and prepare second notice	0.10	0	1000	0	1000	100
8	Pull from overdue file and prepare third notice	0.10	0	0	580	580	58
9	Gold-tab, Xerox, special handling	1.11	0	0	500	500	555
						Total	11,484

** Frequencies are based on the Fall, 1963 semester.

* Time Estimates are based on time studies where the sample sizes measured in number of overdues are 81 for pulling from the overdue file, 233 for pulling from the circulation file, 662 for searching the snag box, 750 for sorting by floor and search, 240 for taping, dating, and sorting, 248 for photo-copying, cutting, and mailing, 248 for filing in the overdue file, and 107 for tabbing, pulling and Xeroxing.

18

Total labor costs can now be calculated using the procedure described in the Memo on Calculating Effective Labor Costs. An effective hourly cost of $1.19 was obtained, producing a total semester labor cost equal to:

$$\frac{\text{Labor cost}}{\text{per Semester}} = \frac{\text{Fixed + Variable man-minutes}}{\text{Minutes per hour}} \quad X \quad \frac{\text{Effective cost}}{\text{per hour}}$$

$$= \frac{507 + 11,484}{60} \quad X \quad \$1.19 = \$237.70$$

Since there were 2880 notices sent in the fall semester of 1964 (1600 first notices, 750 second notices, and 530 third notices), the total material cost of sending notices that semester was about $267. In addition to the cost of notices, there is a cost of $0.02 for Xeroxing each of the 500 gold-tabbed notices. The total material cost is $267 + $10 = $277, producing a total labor and materials cost of:

Labor cost for the semester	$237.70
Material cost for the semester	277.00
Total cost for processing overdues	$514.70

One of the recommended changes in the above system was to eliminate the second and third overdue notices. The possibility of this change was suggested by experiences of other libraries (see, for example, "Fines, Fees, and Overdues", Library Journal, v. 86, no. 6, p. 1105 by Juliette A. Trainor and Gladys E. Eckhardt), and by the relatively few returns that might be ascribed directly to the second and third notices. The number of overdue books returned as a direct result of the second overdue notice is a difficult measurement to obtain. A book returned shortly after the second notice was sent might be the result of the first notice, or the patron's whim, or any of many other reasons. However, as an approximate upper bound on the returns due directly to the second notice, we use the books returned between the second and third notices; and as an approximate upper bound on the returns due directly to the third notice, we use the books returned between the third notice and gold tabbing. The bounds are approximate because some books returned later than the third notice may be attributable to the second notice, and some books returned after gold-tabbing may be attributable

19

to the third notice. On the other hand, as was noted above, it would seem reasonable to assume that many of the books counted in the measurement were returned for reasons other than the reception of the second or third notice. Table E presents the pertinent comparative information on the different notices.

Table E

Comparative Information on First, Second and Third Overdue Notices
University of Michigan General Library, Fall Semester, 1963

Notice	1	2	3	Gold tabbed
Number sent	1600	750	530	500
Upper bound on resulting returns in following week	850	220	30	
Percent effectiveness	53%	29%	6%	
Percent of total overdues returned as a result	53%	14%	2%	
Relative cost of sending overdues per book returned	100	181	940	
Percent of total overdue notices cost	56%	26%	18%	

In other words, the second notices entail one-fourth of the cost while producing less than one-seventh of the returns; and the third notices entail one-sixth of the cost while producing one-fiftieth of the returns. This low return for the dollar, coupled with the philosophy that it is the patron's responsibility to return books, led to the recommendation that the third notice certainly should be eliminated and that the second notice should be considered for elimination. In order to correctly predict the cost changes resulting from eliminating either the second or third notices, we need to determine the cost of the special handling process following gold-tabbing. However, this aspect of the problem was determined by administration to be outside the scope of this study due to its high variability and to its sensitive nature. For lack of these estimates, and other reasons, only the third notices were eliminated.

A second method improvement was recommended, namely Xeroxing rather than photo-copying the notices. The $.02 per copy reduction in materials cost achieved by using Xerox rather than the photocopy method more than offset the slightly higher labor cost of

Xerox and produced a more readable notice as well. These savings
are taken into account in the cost of the proposed systems in Table F.

Table F presents the comparative costs for the old system
and the two alternative proposed systems, one eliminating the second
and third notices and the other eliminating only the third. In all cases the cost incurred after gold-tabbing is not considered, a cost
that is likely to be higher in the proposed systems. Labor is valued
at $1.19 per hour. Times and frequencies are obtained from Table
D.

Patron Service

The time during which a book is in circulation can be divided
into two parts: the first, during which the book is being used; and
the second part, after the patron has finished with the book but before he has returned it to the library. In some cases the patron
may not finish using the book by the end of the charge-out period
and attempt to renew it or turn it in late. In other cases he may
finish it early but wait until the due date to return it. Or he may
return it soon after finishing it. Other considerations aside, it is
desirable to minimize the time between finishing the book and returning it, since that increases its availability to other patrons.
Theoretically, the charge-out period should match the use period as
closely as possible.

However, it would seem there is a trade-off. Changing the
length of the charge-out period would probably affect both the number of patrons not finished using the book at the end of the charge-
out period and the average time between finishing the book and returning it. Lengthening the charge-out time should decrease the number of unfinished uses at the end of the period and vice-versa. The
large number of renewals (26% of the books charged out) suggests
there is considerable justification for lengthening the charge-out
period.

On the other hand, lengthening the charge-out period would
tend to increase the number of times patrons seeking the book would
not find it because it was checked out. This is particularly objec-
tionable in those cases where the book has been finished but not

21

Table F

Task Description	Old System 3 Notices, photo-copy			Proposed System 2 Notices, Xerox			Proposed System 1 Notice, Xerox		
	Variable Labor	Fixed Labor	Materials	Variable Labor	Fixed Labor	Materials	Variable Labor	Fixed Labor	Materials
1 Pull charge slip from Circulation	$ 7.08			$ 7.08			7.08		
2 Search snag box	55.45			44.59			29.26		
3 Send, search in stacks return	114.24	$ 0.72		95.64	$ 0.72		65.58	$ 0.72	
4 Date, tape, sort	12.30			9.33			X		
5 Photoduplicate, cut, stuff, mail	18.84	7.32	$267.80	X			X		
5a Xerox, cut, stuff, mail	X			16.31	7.32	$171.55	11.49	7.32	$116.80
6 Return slip, file in over-due file	5.71	0.72		4.66	0.72		3.15	0.72	
7 Pull overdue, prepare second notice	1.98			1.98			X		
8 Pull overdue, prepare third notice	1.15			X			X		
9 Gold-tab, Xerox, after 1 week	11.01			X			X		
9a Gold-tab, Xerox, after 1 1/2 - 2 weeks	X	1.31	10.00	11.67	1.31	10.60	14.26	1.31	15.00
Sub-totals	$227.76	$10.07	$277.80	$191.26	$10.07	$182.15	$130.82	$10.07	$131.80
	Total $515.63			Total $383.48			Total $272.69		

22

returned. The degree to which this would be the case depends upon patron habits, and particularly upon the number of patrons who are in the habit of waiting until the due date to return a book. This third sub-study concentrated on determining the length of time it takes a user to return a book to the library after he has finished using it.

An attempt was made to obtain this data by asking patrons the question directly in a questionnaire. Since the answers obtained may have been biased the bias was estimated by asking another related question for which objective data was available for checking, namely the total time the book is charged-out. To some extent, the validity of the answers to this related question can be used as a guide in determining the validity of the original question.

Accordingly, a questionnaire was given out to students as they entered the library. (A copy of the questionnaire is found in Appendix A.) The important question on the form is the first one: how long does the user usually take to finish the book? By combining the answers to this question with those to the second question, which asks about the length of time between finishing a book and returning it, one can estimate a return pattern. This estimated pattern is then compared to the actual pattern, which is determined by analyzing a sample of cancelled charge slips. If the two patterns are similar, then the answers can be considered to be relatively unbiased; if they do not compare well, then some bias exists, and less faith can be placed in the answers.

In the detailed analysis of the answers to the user survey, a large number of assumptions had to be made in order to estimate a return pattern. (The data from the survey are found in Appendix G.) For the first question, covering the length of time the book is used, it was assumed that an equal number of users finished each day within the time period; e. g. , if 12 people said they usually finished in 0-3 days, this was treated as three people finishing on each of the first four days that they had the book out. The "3-10 days" group was treated as one-seventh of the number in that group for each of the fourth through the tenth days, and the "10-14 days" group was treated as one-quarter of the number in that group for each of the

23

eleventh through the fourteenth days.

For the second question, each type of answer was translated
into the number of days of lag, or into the day returned. Of those
who said that they returned books right away, one-third were assumed to mean the same day they finished, and two-thirds were assumed to mean the next day. Of those who said they returned the
books at their earliest convenience, one-third were assumed to mean
the same day, one-third to mean the next day, one-sixth to mean
two days later, and one-sixth to mean three days later. By combining these proportions with those from the first question, one can estimate a return pattern. For example, of a group saying that they use
books 0-3 days and return them right away, part of the pattern would
be found as follows: one-quarter finish on the same day they check
the book out, and one-third of these users return the book on the
same day; therefore, one-twelfth of this group are assumed to return books on the same day that they have checked them out. Similarly, the patterns for this group on the next, second, third, and fourth
days may be found to be one-fourth, one-fourth, one-fourth, and one-
sixth, respectively.

One exception to this method was made: this was that those
proportions which were indicated to be returned after the fourteenth
day were instead assigned to the fourteenth day, since those users
who were usually fined were to indicate such as their response to
the second question.

Of those users who answered that they returned books in order to avoid a fine, it was assumed that one-third returned books on
the thirteenth day, and two-thirds on the fourteenth, regardless of
the length of time they actually used the books.

Further adjustment was made according to the number of
books borrowed per semester, in order to weigh more heavily the
answers of those who checked out more books. The number of an-
sers in each group was accordingly multiplied by the average number of books checked out per semester by each user.

The results of this method for estimating a return pattern,
based on the data given in Appendix G, are given in Appendix H, and

are graphed in Appendix B and C.

In order to determine whether bias existed in the results of the user survey, the return pattern as found above had to be compared with the actual return pattern. This actual pattern was determined by studing a large sample of the charge slips. These were returned to the library along with the books, and the return dates were stamped on the slips. By comparing each date returned with the date due, the number of days each book was out could easily be determined. Data from this sample are given in Appendix I and are graphed in Appendix D.

Having estimated the return pattern according to the survey answers and having determined the actual pattern from charge slips, the next step was to use this data in establishing a pattern for the length of time a book is actually used. Appendix B shows that the patrons indicate they return the books much later than the charge slips say they do. Assuming the charge slip data fairly represents the sample obtained from the survey, the source of the discrepency between the answers to the survey and the actual pattern is that the users have made an error either in estimating how long it takes them to return books after they have finished them, how long they actually use books, or a combination of these. Appendix D shows the pattern of book use length as given in the survey returns. This would be the actual use pattern if the error in returns lay in the answers to the question on how long it takes to return books after they have been used. This pattern has also been adjusted to account for the discrepancy between the survey returns and the actual book-return pattern. This adjusted pattern represents the use pattern if the error lies in the estimated length of time the books are used. Added to the two curves thus obtained are two more curves which represent a one-day tolerance in either direction. This is to allow for error in the following areas: sampling error in the user survey, sampling error in the charge slip tabulation, error in assumptions made in determining the book-return pattern from the survey, and reinforcing errors in the answers to the survey questions. It is probable that the actual pattern for length of use lies in between these latter two curves.

Conclusions

Now that renewal costs and frequency (about 2¢ per renewal and 26% of the charge-outs eligible for first renewal) have been obtained, overdue costs (about 18¢ per overdue) obtained, and user book return habits estimated, the goal is to relate these factors for various charge-out periods. For example, a lengthening of the charge-out period to three weeks would lower renewal and overdue costs by a certain amount, and a social benefit would result from users not having to renew books as often; however, there would be a decrease in service due to a large number of books being out and therefore unavailable to users.

However, such an analysis was not made for several reasons. First, the validity of the survey data is highly questionable, as is revealed in the discrepency between the survey and charge slip data. To correct this would mean redoing the survey and paying closer statistical attention to sample sizes and possibly asking the patrons to respond with respect to a specific book they have recently returned rather than with respect to their habits in general, but of course these changes would not guarantee validity. A second problem is the difficulty in predicting changes that different charge-out periods might have on use patterns. We were not able to locate any data from similar libraries with different charge-out periods for comparison.

The third and possibly most telling problem hindering the analysis was the inability to compare the dollar costs of the overdue and renewal processes to the dollar benefits of better service. One approach might be to assign dollar costs to increased service by determining the increases in the purchasing budget necessary to increase collection size so that book availability is the same under all systems. However, this involves a fairly sophisticated statistical argument (using techniques of queuing theory) that would involve considerably more data collection in various areas of the collection, and so was deemed outside the scope of this project considering the other inadequacies of the study.

Finally, not all costs were quantified. As mentioned above,

special handling of long-overdues was not analyzed, and, in addition, the costs of placing holds on books was ignored.

Even though for the above reasons comparable costs and benefits cannot be predicted in precise fashion for the different charge-out periods, some general observations can be made from the data which are relevant to the question at hand--the optimal charge-out period:

1. A very large number of books are now renewed, indicating that an increased charge-out period would be well received by the patrons.

2. Appendix D shows that less than one-half the books charged out are completed by the tenth day, indicating that a shortening of the charge-out period is undesirable except in a situation of high, short-term demand.

3. The dollar cost of processing renewals and overdues each semester ($300 for renewals and, under the proposed system, approximately $300 for overdues) is small enough that it is probably not a major factor in the decision.

4. Table G indicates that a considerable number of students do wait until the due date to return books, a habit which might very likely continue if the charge-out period were lengthened.

Three changes discussed in this study were implemented:

1. The charge-out period was lengthened from two to three weeks largely on the basis of justification #1 (renewals) above. This change has been accompanied by carefully selective overnight and reserve book policy.

2. The third overdue notice was eliminated.

3. Overdue notices are now Xeroxed rather than photocopied.

Systems Analysis in a University Library

Appendix A
Library User Survey

This survey is a means to help the library improve its service. Your cooperation in giving us the following information will enable us to provide better service to you in the future.

Check the square that most closely corresponds with the usual time it takes you to finish a book you have borrowed from the University of Michigan General Library.

___ 0 - 3 days

___ 3 - 10 days

___10 - 14 days

___usually have to renew the book to finish it

Check the square that best describes why you return a book you have borrowed from the University of Michigan General Library when you do:

___ I make a point to return it right away

___ I return my books at my earliest convenience

___ I return my books in order to avoid a fine

___ I am usually fined for overdue books

How many books did you borrow last semester?

___ less than 10

___ 10 - 35

___ over 35

Check:

___ Graduate student

___ Undergraduate student

Please return this questionnaire to the box near the west stairway.

Thank you.

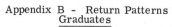

Appendix B - Return Patterns
Graduates
<u>Cumulative</u>

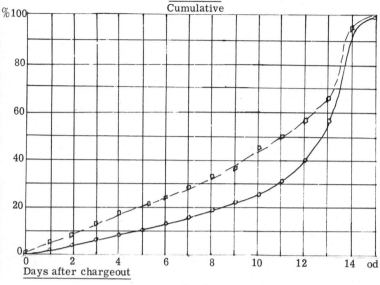

Days after chargeout

Individual

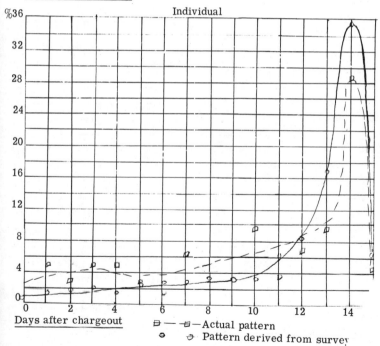

Days after chargeout

⊟ — ⊟ —Actual pattern
⊙   ⊝ Pattern derived from survey

29

Appendix C
Undergraduates
Cumulative

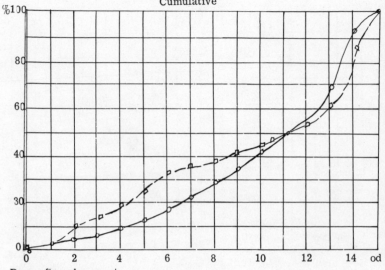

Days after chargeout

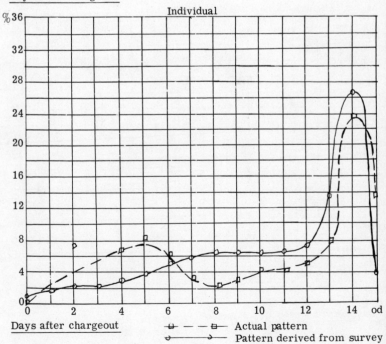

Individual

Days after chargeout

—☐— — —☐— Actual pattern

—○— — —○— Pattern derived from survey

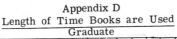

Appendix D
Length of Time Books are Used

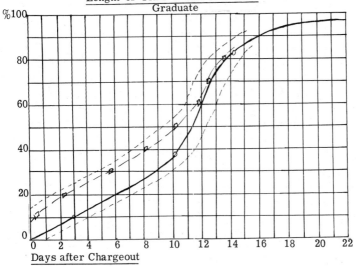

Graduate

Days after Chargeout

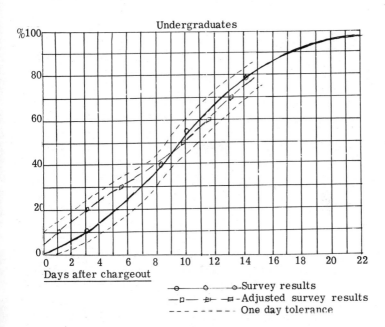

Undergraduates

Days after chargeout

—o——o——o—Survey results
—□——□——□—-Adjusted survey results
— — — — — — One day tolerance

Appendix G
Data from User Survey

	Graduates				Undergraduates			
I. Less than 10	0-3	3-10	10-14	Re	0-3	3-10	10-14	Re
Right away	0	3	1	1	3	12	7	0
Earliest convenience	0	7	4	3	11	29	9	3
Avoid a fine	2	5	4	1	1	16	9	7
Usually overdue	0	0	0	1	0	0	0	0
II. 10-35								
Right away	2	7	3	0	2	6	5	0
Earliest convenience	2	10	8	4	2	16	7	3
Avoid a fine	1	7	7	6	3	7	5	6
Usually overdue	1	0	1	1	0	2	0	1
III. Over 35								
Right away	1	0	3	1	0	3	0	3
Earliest convenience	2	4	14	3	1	4	2	4
Avoid a fine	0	1	4	1	0	1	1	1
Usually overdue	1	1	1	1	0	0	1	0

Appendix H
Return Pattern Indicated by User Survey Results

No. of days out	Graduates		Undergraduates	
	%	Cum.%	%	Cum.%
0	0.7	0.7	0.7	0.7
1	1.7	2.4	1.7	2.4
2	1.9	4.3	2.0	4.4
3	2.1	6.4	2.2	6.6
4	1.7	8.1	2.2	8.8
5	2.2	10.3	3.9	12.7
6	2.8	13.1	5.1	17.8
7	3.0	16.1	5.5	23.3
8	3.3	19.4	6.2	29.5
9	3.3	22.7	6.2	35.7
10	3.3	26.0	6.2	41.9

			Optimal Charge-Out Period	
11	6.2	32.2	7.1	49.0
12	8.6	40.8	6.6	55.6
13	16.9	57.7	13.8	69.4
14	35.7	93.4	26.7	96.1
Overdue	6.6	100.0	3.9	100.0

Appendix I

Data from Charge Slips

No. of days Out	Graduates			Undergraduates		
	No.	%	Cum.%	No.	%	Cum.%
0	2	0.7	0.7	0	0.0	0.0
1	15	5.0	5.7	7	2.2	2.2
2	9	3.0	8.7	23	7.3	9.5
3	15	5.0	13.7	7	2.2	11.7
4	15	5.0	18.7	20	6.3	18.0
5	8	2.6	21.3	26	8.2	26.2
6	5	1.6	22.9	19	6.0	32.2
7	19	6.3	29.2	10	3.2	35.4
8	14	4.6	33.8	7	2.2	37.6
9	10	3.3	37.1	10	3.2	40.8
10	29	9.6	46.7	14	4.5	45.3
11	11	3.6	50.3	13	4.1	49.4
12	21	7.0	57.3	16	5.1	54.5
13	29	9.6	66.9	25	7.9	62.4
14	87	28.8	95.7	75	23.7	86.1
Overdue	13	4.3	100.0	44	13.9	100.0
Total	302			316		

Investigation of a Standardized Circulation System
for the Divisional Libraries
By: M. C. Drott, C. G. Uligian, D. A. Wood

Objective:

The objectives of this project were twofold: first to investigate current circulation procedures in the divisional libraries; second to evaluate several circulation procedures in terms of cost and appropriateness for the libraries involved.

Background:

The divisional libraries have either grown from departmental collections or been split from the main library collection. Each has a great deal of autonomy in developing systems and procedures and thus each has circulation procedures that are to some extent unique. This study was first suggested by the library's Substitute Service, a department charged with providing clerical replacements for divisional library personnel who are sick or on vacation. This job is greatly complicated by the fact that training in one library may not be applicable in another.

Investigation:

Each divisional librarian was interviewed. The results of this investigation are presented in the chart below.

The most prevalent of the existing circulation systems consists of a book card system with several charging periods. All divisional libraries have two week and overnight charges for students, and some of them also have one week or three day charges. Most divisionals operate with an indefinite charging period for staff members, but there are exceptions.

The charging procedure requires that the borrower write his name, address and telephone number on a book card which is located inside each book. He presents the book, book card, and his student identification to the clerk at the desk. Both book card and book are stamped with the date due. The clerk retains the book card and at the end of the day places a metal tab on the top to indicate the due date. The book card is then filed in the circulation file. To discharge a book the clerk simply pulls the book card from the circulation file and cancels the date due on both book and card. The book card is replaced in the pocket in the back of the book card and the book is reshelved.

Cards for overdue books are generally pulled from the file twice a week. These cards are located by the color coded metal tabs afixed to them. The date code is unique with each library. Once the overdue cards are pulled, the tabs are removed and if the cards are not already in call number order, they are put in that order. The overdues are then searched for in the stacks to check for clerical discharging errors. Following the search, the cards are put into alphabetical order by borrower's name, and overdue notices are sent. The percentage of books that are overdue varies from about 2% to 35% and seems to be directly related to the strictness of fine collection. This relationship may not be causal since in some libraries the faculty (who are never fined) account for a large percentage of the overdues.

The most prevalent system for charging reserve books operates by using a long form on which the student signs his name. This form is kept inside the book and lists the author, title and call number typed on the top of the card, much like a book card. The card is used approximately twenty-five times before it must be replaced. The card is filed in a special vertical reserve file during the loan period.

In order to evaluate alternate charging systems a test circulation file was prepared. This file consisted of about 600 charge records. (This number was chosen to represent a library processing about 15,000 charges per year). Times were collected using subjects who had no previous library experience. All of the times presented are averages. In cases where time depends on the physical arrangement of the library (such as searching) the step has been omitted.

Brooklyn System. The Brooklyn circulation system is a transaction slip system which uses a specialized filing technique. This technique eliminates both tabbing and additional files, but still makes

it possible to keep track of overdues. This is accomplished by inter-
filing by date within the call number. That is, all slips are filed by
call number index divisions and by date within the index divisions.
A study was conducted and the optimal size of each index division
was found to be 60 charges. This means that prior to converting to
such a circulation system it would be necessary to determine from
the present circulation where the index divisions should be set such
that approximately 60 charges per index division would result.

The table below presents the times for performing the various steps of this system.

It should be noted that in order to file by date within the index division one simply places each charge in the very front of each
division as they are charged. By doing so, the overdues will accumulate at the back of each index division since they will be the oldest
charges in the file. This means that filing time will be reduced as
will the time required to pull overdues from the circulation file.

However, this system has two disadvantages. First, the filing
operation is greatly complicated unless it is possible to charge all
books within each library for one common circulation period, such
as two weeks. Second, the time required to search in the circulation file by call number to see if a particular book has been checked out is much greater under this system than the other two since
the slips are not in absolute call number order. The mean time to
perform this operation is 6/10 of a minute; and it may be done as
often as once per hour in the larger divisionals.

From a cost standpoint, this system takes less time for
charging, discharging, and handling overdues than the other two
systems studies. However, acceptance of the system would encounter
difficulty because of its differences from anything presently in use,
and the fact that the book cards are not exactly located.

Two-File System. The two-file circulation system utilizes a
transaction slip. Both halves of the slip are retained at the circulation desk; one is filed by call number in the circulation file, the
other is filed by due date in a file which is indexed from one to
thirty-one. The due date file is used to expedite the overdue process.

Systems Analysis in a University Library

Brooklyn System (50-60 cards/division)

Charging:	time/book (min.)	totals
1. Check information on slip	.265	
2. Check identification card	.050	
3. Date stamp transaction slip		
4. Tear slips apart		
5. Slip in overdue slip	.120	
6. Set aside front slip		
7. Sort by division	.047	
8. File in circulation file	.052	.534

Discharging:		
1. Pull slip from book	.046	
2. Pull slip from circulation file	.205	
		.251

Overdues:		
1. Pull from circulation file	.059	
2. Notify (average time)	1.000	
3. Refile	.030	
		1.089

Assuming 20% overdues, total time per book = 1.003

File Query: .594

Average (4 request/day) = 2.376 min./day

Material Cost: (per 1000 charges)

Transaction slip (#7900)

$$\frac{\$5.76}{1000 \text{ slips}} \times \frac{1 \text{ slip}}{1 \text{ chg.}} = \$5.76$$

To pull overdues, it is only necessary to pull out all charge slips
remaining in the file section corresponding to the date. However,
for this added convenience additional handling is necessary. At the
charge-out point the additional filing required is very little, since
the daily charge slips need only be placed in the file section corresponding to the due date. (Since they will be sorted by call number
before the two forms are separated, within the date due they will be
sequenced by call number.) At the discharge points, however, an additional operation is necessary. After the first half of the transaction slip has been obtained from the circulation file, the second half
must be obtained from the due date file. This additional time is reflected in the total discharging time for the system. It should be
realized that this system speeds up the overdue process at the cost

Divisional Library	Document	Due Date Identification	Circulation	
			Filing Procedure	'62 -'63 Total Volume
Architecture	book card	metal tabs	call number	15,776
Asia	transaction slip	none	call number	3,600
Chemistry-Pharmacy	book card	metal tab	by author	8,813
Dentistry	book card	metal tab	by author	17,797
Education	transaction slip	two-file system	call number & due date	21,601
Engineering	book card	metal tab	call number	39,200
Fine Arts	book card	metal tab	call number	9,052
Bureau of Government	book card	metal tab	by author	6,812
Library Science	book card & transaction slip for each book	metal tab	by author	13,000
Mathematics	book card	metal tab	by author	18,000
Music	book card & transaction slip	metal tab	call number	13,424
Natural Science	book card & transaction slip to get from stacks	metal tab	call number	26,285
Phoenix	book card	metal tab	by author & call no.	11,475
Physics-Astronomy	book card	metal tab	by author	22,700
Public Health	book card	metal tab	by author	6,400
Social Work	book card	metal tab	call number	14,000
Transportation* (since combined with Engineering)	book card	metal tab	call number	2,500-3,000

Faculty Circulation Periods	Student Circulation Periods	Reserves Open or Closed	Size of Collection
indefinite	2 week	closed	400
indefinite	2 week	none	none
indefinite	overnight 2 week	closed	300
indefinite	3 day - 1 week - 2 week	closed	150
dept. faculty —semester other faculty —like student	overnight 1 week 2 week	closed	1100
indefinite 2 weeks	overnight - 1 day - 2 week	closed	1050
Indefinite	overnight 2 week	open & closed	750
2 weeks	overnight 2 week	open	1325
indefinite	overnight - 3 day - 1 week - 2 week	open	1500
indefinite 4 weeks	overnight - 3 day - 2 week	closed	300
dept. fac. — indefinite other fac. —like student	overnight 2 week	open & closed	9000 (reference)
overnight 2 week - 4 week 1 year	overnight 1 day - 3 day 2 week	closed	500-600
indefinite	overnight 2 week	open	60-70
semester - 2 month 4 week	overnight 2 week	closed	200
indefinite	overnight 3 day - 1 week	closed	150-200
overnight & indefinite	overnight 1 week - 2 week	open & closed	1800
indefinite	overnight 3 day - 2 week	open & closed	150

Appendix D - continued

Divisional Library	Reserves	Overdues		
	Charging Document	Frequency of Notification	Means of Notification	No. of Notices
Architecture	book card	daily	post cards & letter	4
Asia	none	weekly	post cards	2
Chemistry-Pharmacy	long form	every two days	post cards & letter	3
Dentistry	long form	twice a week	post cards & costed list	2
Education	identification card & special slip	twice a week	post cards & letter	3
Engineering	identification card & book card	twice a week	post cards	3
Fine Arts	transaction slip	daily	post cards	4
Bureau of Government	book card	daily	post cards, letter, telephone	3
Library Science	room use slip	daily	post cards, & telephone	3
Mathematics	long form	every two days	post cards & letter	3
Music	long form	every three days	post cards	4
Natural Science	room use form	every two days	post cards & telephone	4
Phoenix	none	daily	post cards & telephone	3
Physics-Astronomy	long form	twice a week	post cards & telephone	5
Public Health	room use slip	daily	telephone	2
Social Work	long form	twice a week	post cards & telephone	3
Transportation* (since combined with Engineering)	long form	every two weeks	post cards	1

Fine Collection	Staffing			Collection	
	Students	Clerical	Professional	Number of Titles	Number of Periodicals
lenient	162 hrs./wk	1	2	20,000	200
strict	58 hrs./wk	2	7	125,543	620
semi-strict	30 hrs./wk	1	1/2	29,000	400
none	50 hrs./wk	1	1	21,439	400
strict	110 hrs./wk 220 hrs./summer wk	3	1	30,000	570
lenient	142 hrs./wk	2	3/4	145,000	2,500
semi-strict	55 hrs./wk	2	1	18,000	135
strict	15 hrs./wk	0	3	49,815	249
strict	80 hrs./wk	4 (part time)	1	18,000	850
semi-strict	30 hrs./wk	2	1/2	33,000	500
lenient	100 hrs./wk	3	1	17-20,000; 6-7,000 in Gen. Lib.	67
semi-strict	70 hrs./wk	1	2	?	5,934
lenient	none	1	1/2	41,021	4,023
lenient	50 hrs./wk	1	1	40,000	600
none	68 hrs./wk	1	1	16,000	177
semi-strict	67 hrs./wk	1	1/2	6,300	115
none	20 hrs./wk	2 (20 hrs./wk)	1-1/2	200,000	60,000

of additional time expended in charging and discharging. If there were no overdues, this system would not be efficient; in fact, the second file would be completely useless. However, at present an average of twenty percent of the books circulated in the divisional libraries are returned overdue.

An advantage of this system and the Brooklyn system is the use of a transaction slip. If either of these two systems were initiated, the borrower would have the convenience of knowing that no matter what library on campus he went into he would charge a book out by using a transaction slip. As the situation is now, a borrower must read signs and ask questions to find what the charging procedure is, since in each library it is different.

From a cost standpoint, a transaction slip costs about the same as a book card. The material cost itself is much greater, but a transaction slip requires no preparation labor as does a book card.

Two-File System

Charging:	time/book(min.)	totals
1. Check information on slip	.265	
2. Check identification card	.050	
3. Open book, date stamp both card & book	.110	
4. Set slip aside	.010	
5. Sort by call number	.087	
6. Separate copies	.035	
7. File in due date file by date	.010	
8. File in circ. file by call number	.118	
		.685

Discharging:		
1. Pull card from circ. file	.150	
2. Pull card from due date file	.092	
3. Open book, cross out due date	.060	
		.302

Overdues:		
1. Pull cards from due date file	.005	
2. Notify	1.000	
3. Refile in due date file	.005	
		1.010

Assuming 20% overdues, total time per book = 1.189

Material Cost: (per 1000 charges)

Transaction slip (#7900)
$$\frac{\$5.76}{1000 \text{ slips}} \text{ X } \frac{1 \text{ slip}}{1 \text{ chg.}} = \quad \$5.76$$

Tabbed-Book Card System. The tabbing system utilizes book cards and metal tabs. (The plastic overlay tabbing system was not thoroughly investigated because of its inability to designate a sufficient number of time periods.) Each book contains a book card inside the back cover. This card is removed from the book and the borrower signs his name and address to charge the book out. On the average, the book card must be replaced every twelfth charge. At the end of each day, a metal tab is placed on each book card to designate the due date and the book cards are filed by call number in the circulation file.

The disadvantage of this system occurs when discharging books. The book card is removed from the circulation file and placed in the pocket in the back cover of the book. On occasion, the wrong book card will inadvertently be placed in a book when discharging it. This is very costly from a labor standpoint for it takes time to find and correct the error. There are also problems with the tabs themselves. They are hard to put on, occasionally fall off, and have to be sorted before they are reused.

There are two advantages of this system. First, most divisional libraries' circulation systems are some form of a book card system and it would be a simple process to convert to a standardized book card system. Second, the book card circulation system is more like presently existing automated circulation systems. Automated systems utilize master cards which are analogous to book cards, except that the information is stored using holes punched in the card. It would be a slightly easier task to convert to an automated system if a book card system were being used, because of the similarity between the two systems.

Tabbed-Book Card System

Charging:	time/book (min.)	totals
1. Check information on card	.140	
2. Check identification card	.050	
3. Open book, date stamp book and information cards	.110	
4. Set card aside	.010	
5. Tab at end of day	.127	

6. File by call number   .140
                                                              .577

Discharging:

1. Pull book card from circulation file   .150
2. Open book, cross out due date   .060
3. Replace book card   .125
                                                              .335

Overdues:

1. Search by tab and pull   .025
2. Retab   .127
3. Notify   1.000
4. Refile in circulation file   .110
                                                             1.262

Assuming 20% overdues, total time per book = 1.164

Material Cost: (per 1000 charges)

  Book card (#4097) - 12 charges/card

$$\frac{\$1.80}{1000 \text{ cards}} \times \frac{1 \text{ card}}{12 \text{ chgs.}} = \$0.15$$

  Book card preparation (labor)

$$\frac{\$.066}{\text{card}} \times \frac{1 \text{ card}}{12 \text{ chgs.}} \times 1000 = \frac{5.55}{\$5.70}$$

  The table below compares the annual cost of each charging system.

Cost Comparison for Circulation Systems in Average Size Divisional
                                   Library
                          (15,000 charges/year)

Brooklyn System: totals

  Labor
$$\frac{15,000 \text{ chg.}}{1 \text{ year}} \times \frac{1.003 \text{ min.}}{1 \text{ charge}} \times \frac{1 \text{ hr.}}{60 \text{ min.}} \times \frac{\$1.75}{\text{hr.}} = \$439.00$$

  Materials:
$$\frac{\$5.76}{1000 \text{ chg.}} \times \frac{15,000 \text{ chg.}}{1 \text{ year}} = \frac{86.40}{\$525.40}$$

Two-File System:

  Labor
$$\frac{15,000 \text{ chg.}}{1 \text{ year}} \times \frac{1.189 \text{ min.}}{1 \text{ charge}} \times \frac{1 \text{ hr.}}{60 \text{ min.}} \times \frac{\$1.75}{\text{hr.}} = \$520.00$$

  Materials:
$$\frac{\$5.76}{\text{chg.}} \times \frac{15,000 \text{ chg.}}{1 \text{ year}} = \frac{86.40}{\$606.40}$$

44

Cost Comparison - continued

Tabbed Book Card System:

Labor

$$\frac{15,000 \text{ chg.}}{1 \text{ year}} \quad X \quad \frac{1.164 \text{ min.}}{1 \text{ charge}} \quad X \quad \frac{1 \text{ hr.}}{60 \text{ min.}} \quad X \quad \frac{\$1.75}{\text{hour}} = \$508.00$$

Material

$$\frac{\$5.70}{1000 \text{ chgs.}} \quad X \quad \frac{15,000 \text{ chgs.}}{1 \text{ year}} \qquad = \quad \underline{85.40}$$

$$\$593.40$$

Conclusions

The cost analysis above shows that the actual differences between circulation systems are slight. This is especially true when we realize that time savings will occur as fractions of a minute scattered throughout the year. Only the most careful management could turn all of this time to other useful tasks.

From preliminary reports it was found that there was much opposition to both the Two-File System and the Brooklyn System from a convenience standpoint. Librarians seemed to think that both systems were a step toward complexity rather than simplicity and would make training and operating procedures more difficult.

In view of these factors, as well as the fact that the use of a book card system would be a step in the direction of an eventual automated system, the Tabbed-Book Card System is recommended.

The most effective tabbing procedure is one which utilizes positions on the book card and different colored tabs to designate due dates. It is advantageous to minimize the number of colors used to simplify handling and sorting operations. It is also advantageous to limit the number of positions used on the book card for clarity. The optimal combination was found to be two book card positions and three rotating tab colors to designate due date. By proper design of the rotation sequence it is possible to tab a book card only once. If the book becomes overdue, a red tab is added on the opposite side to show a notice has been sent. The original tab is left on the book card so that if in another ten days the book is still overdue, the book card will be pulled from the circulation file again and a final notice will be sent.

45

Systems Analysis in a University Library

Tabbing Schedule

Week	Day	Charging Periods 2 wk. tab	1 wk. tab	3 day tab	Pull and Tab other side red
1	Su	C on Right	A on Right	C on Left	
	M	A on Left	B on Right	C on Left	
	T	A on L	B on R	A on R	B on Left
	W	A on L	B on R	A on R	
	Th	B on L	C on R	A on R	
	F	B on L	C on R	A on R	C on L
	S	B on L	C on R	B on R	
2	Su	B on L	C on R	B on R	
	M	C on L	A on L	B on R	
	T	C on L	A on L	C on R	A on R
	W	C on L	A on L	C on R	
	Th	A on R	B on L	C on R	
	F	A on R	B on L	C on R	B on R
	S	A on R	B on L	A on L	
3	Su	A on R	B on L	A on L	
	M	B on R	C on L	B on L	
	T	B on R	C on L	B on L	C on R
	W	B on R	C on L	B on L	
	Th	C on R	A on R	B on L	
	F	C on R	A on R	B on L	A on L
	S	C on R	A on R	C on L	
4	Su	C on R	A on R	C on L	

Using three colors--A, B, and C.

The use of a tabbing system which uses two positions prevents the file tray of cards from becoming lopsided due to the thickness of the tabs on one side.

Under the proposed schedule presented above, books charged for 3-days that become overdue will be notified one to three days after the due date. One-week and two-weeks books will be handled two to four days after they become due. On the basis of a previous study, it is recommended that only two overdue notices and a final letter be sent.

The reserve system recommended is that originated by the Engineering Library and also later adopted by the Education Library. This system utilizes the book card in the back of the book and the student's identification card. The borrower need do no writing or filling out of forms to charge a book for room use under this system; all he must do is hand the clerk his student identification card. The clerk takes the identification card and the book card from the book and places them together in a folder and files them alphabetically by the student's last name. If the student wishes to charge more than one book, the book cards from the other books are filed in the same folder with the student identification card. If a student wishes to charge a reserve book overnight, he must fill out the book card for this purpose and his student identification card is returned.

This system has met with much success. The greatest advantage is the increased control over reserve books. The books are never left on the tables, for the student must return the book to the desk to obtain his identification card. An additional advantage is that less staff time is required to charge and discharge a reserve book than in any reserve system presently being used. The borrower, of course, also does less work and the charging and discharging takes less of his time.

When a book is requested to be put on reserve, little must be done since the book card is already in the book and no additional forms are needed. The only operation needed is to make a notation in the card catalog. In most systems, all or many of the following operations must be accomplished: a long card is typed to insert in the book, the book card is pulled from the book and is placed in the circulation file, the book is taped or starred on the outside cover to designate it as a reserve book in case it is left on the tables (so that it will not be reshelved in the stacks), and a notation is made in the card catalog. The process of taking a book off reserve is also expedited by the recommended system.

Conclusions:

Several charging systems have a lower cost than the tab system recommended for adoption. But the lack of a general consensus in their favor precludes their use. Since there are no great economic incentives, it seems that standardization can only be achieved through group action or executive fiat. The promotion of greater communication between divisional librarians might also result in the quicker application of other solutions to library problems developed by individual divisional librarians.

Development of Methods and Time Standards for a Large Scale Library
Inventory

By: R. E. Beck, J. R. McKinnon

Objective:

The purpose of this study was to investigate the problems
that would be encountered in making an inventory of the General Library. A general procedure was to be developed for conducting the
inventory which would economically provide the desired information
and create minimum disruption of daily library operations.

Development of Inventory Procedure:

The procedure was designed first because the type and quantity of problems and the practicability of conducting the inventory de-
pend upon the procedure. A procedure is an arrangement of functions
intended to achieve some objective. The principal objective of any
library inventory is the determination of all library holdings which
are missing from the shelves for reasons other than legitimate use
or location elsewhere in the library system. In designing a procedure
two steps are necessary: first, finding out what functions will be
needed in a procedure; second, putting together the functions so discovered.

In developing a method satisfying the specific needs of the
General Library, a detailed investigation was made into the basic inventory activities conducted in the past, both in divisional libraries
and within the General Library itself. A thorough explanation was
provided of the methods and procedures used in yearly inventories
in the Undergraduate Library. Helpful information and statistics were
supplied from the inventory of selected stack sections which was conducted in 1958-1959. Technical information relating to cataloging procedures used throughout the library system was provided. Special emphasis was placed on the problems which would be encountered in
attempting to conduct an inventory of the General Library.

From the above information, the following necessary functions
were discovered and organized into a procedure:

(1) A shel<u>f readin</u>g <u>phas</u>e to ascertain which books listed in the shelf list are not on the shelves.

(2) A <u>preliminary</u> <u>circulation</u> <u>file</u> <u>check</u> to determine which volumes and/or copies listed as missing from the shelves are signed out or otherwise accounted for elsewhere in the system.

(3) A <u>catalog</u> <u>searching</u> <u>activity</u> to obtain the complete record of holdings when the shelf list records must be supplemented by official catalog or check list verification.

(4) A <u>waiting</u> <u>period</u> which allows time for books which were off the shelves during the first shelf check to be reshelved by the Circulation Department and stacks personnel.

(5) A <u>second</u> <u>shelf</u> <u>check</u>, after which the remaining inventory cards representing copies and volumes not yet located are considered to be missing.

(6) A <u>final</u> <u>circulation</u> <u>file</u> <u>check</u>, after which holdings unaccounted for are assumed to be missing.

Completion of the last step in this procedure leaves a group of snags and a list of missing books which require rechecking and final evaluation by specially trained workers and library staff.

One observes that the six functions above can be viewed as objectives for which procedures must be developed. But before we develop these procedures, we see that specific information must pass from one function to another in the above six functions. This information must be tightly controlled if we are to have an accurate and effective inventory procedure. The "inventory control card" was developed for this reason. It represents a record of all the results of shelf checking which can be readily interpreted by other personnel at later stages of the inventory procedure. Although recording information by this method during shelf checking is time-consuming, the card format makes the other operations easier, and ultimately, less expensive. The cards also provide a method for sorting and channeling the information into the next required inventory process.

When an inventory card needs to be filled out, the call numbers and the author's last name and initials are recorded in the allotted spaces. When the shelf list card indicates "See Official

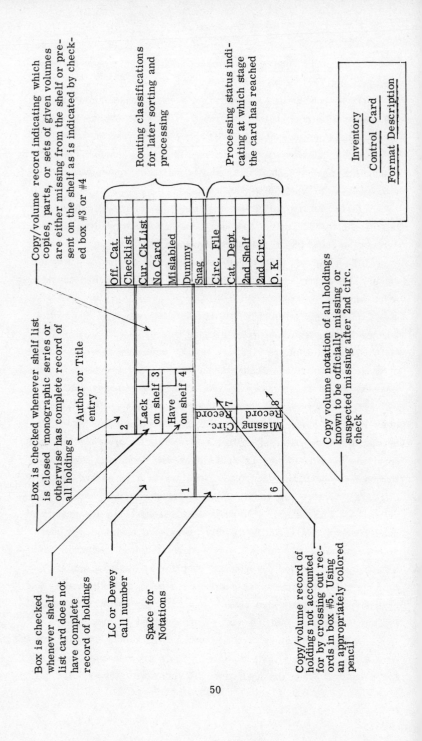

Catalog," or "See Check List," the box corresponding to "Have on Shelf" is checked and the volumes and/or copies on the shelves are appropriately recorded. Otherwise, the card reader determines what volumes and/or copies are lacking on the shelves and records them appropriately in box number five.

At the circulation file the entries that are circulating are recorded in the "Circulation Record" space if the inventory card is marked "Have on Shelf." Otherwise, the checked out entries are slashed out in the "Lack on Shelf" section with a red ball-point pen. All cards that have been processed in the circulation file will have the "Circ. File" box checked. If during this process all entries are accounted for, the "O. K." status box is checked.

The cards are next sorted by the routing classifications indicated by the end boxes. Any inventory cards which must be verified in the Catalog Department are separated at this stage and sent to cataloging before going through the second shelf check. If the entries on the card marked "Have on Shelf" have all been accounted for in the Catalog Department, the "O. K." box is checked. All cards processed in the Catalog Department will have the "Cat. Dept." box checked. All inventory cards that are suspected missing are processed through the second shelf check and circulation check, during which time the appropriate boxes are checked. (See accompanying diagram "Format Description".)

			Off. Cat.	
			Checklist	
	Lack on shelf		Cur. Ck List	
			No Card	
	Have on shelf		Mislabeled	
			Dummy	
	Circ. Record		Snag	
			Circ. File	
			Cat. Dept.	
Missing Record			2nd Shelf	
			2nd Circ.	
			O. K.	

Format Description
Inventory Control Card   (actual size)

Now, the complete procedure can be developed. The functions with their procedures are described below:

I. <u>Shelf List Reading</u> - (two-person teams required)

    A. Team elects drawer.

    B. Team fills out two slips with drawer number and call numbers contained in that drawer and gives one to supervisor.

    C. Team goes to stacks and locates correct section.

    D. Team gets necessary equipment.

        1. Chairs, step-ups, book carts

        2. Inventory cards and <u>black</u> ball-point pen

    E. One person reads cards while other searches shelves.

        1. Card reader thumbs through cards until he comes to General Library (GL) card.

            (a) Card stamped "See Official Catalog" or "See Current Check List" or "See Check List"

                (1) Reads complete call number and asks for the volumes and/or copies on the shelves; checks box "Have on Shelf"

                (2) Fills out inventory card with this information

            (b) Otherwise, reads complete call number, reading also the volume and/or copies that should be on the shelf, and waits for the shelf searcher's response

                (1) Shelf-searcher responds, "Here"

                    a. Reads next GL card

                (2) Shelf-searcher responds, "Missing"

                    a. Fills out inventory card with volumes and/or copies that are not on the shelf; checks box "Lack on Shelf"

                    b. Reads next GL card

                (3) Shelf-searcher checks call number inside book.

                    i. If mislabeled, fills out inventory card, checking "Mislabeled" box

       i. If mislabeled, fills out inventory card, checking "Mislabeled" box

      ii. Removes book from shelf and puts inventory card inside cover

    b. Card-reader checks for number.

       i. If unable to find, fills out inventory card checking "No Card" box, removes book from shelf, and puts inventory card inside cover

      ii. If unable to find, completes process as above

   (4) Shelf-searcher responds, "Dummy"

    a. Fills out inventory card checking "Dummy" box

  (c) If any problem arises, fills out an inventory card checking "Snag"

F. After completing drawer, team

  1. Replaces equipment

  2. Puts rubber band around filled out inventory cards with drawer slip on top

  3. Takes drawer back to Catalog Department

  4. Takes filled-out inventory cards and books removed from shelves to the supervisor

  5. Selects next drawer and starts through process again

II. Circulation Check

A. Clerk gets filled out inventory cards from supervisor.

B. Clerk gets a red ball-point pen.

C. Clerk goes to circulation file.

D. Clerk asks for circulation slips corresponding to call numbers written on top slip.

E. Clerk compares circulation slips with inventory card:

  1. If there is a circulation slip and no inventory card, pulls circulation slip and treats as a special snag, fills out inventory card accordingly

   2. If there is a circulation slip and an inventory
      card with the same number:
      a. Inventory card indicates "Lack on Shelf"
         (1) Slashes out entries accounted for by the
             circulation slip
         (2) Checks box corresponding to "Circ. File"
      b. Inventory card indicates "Have on Shelf"
         (1) Records those entries found in circula-
             tion on the inventory card in the appro-
             priate space
         (2) Checks box corresponding to "Circ. File"
      c. If when slashing out entries for cards mark-
         ed "Lack on Shelf," all entries are account-
         ed for, checks "O. K."
F. Clerk sorts cards into six groups by routing designations.
   1. Cards marked "Official Catalog"
   2. Cards marked "Check List"
   3. Cards marked "Current Check List"
   4. Cards marked "Dummy"
   5. Cards marked "O. K."
   6. All other cards marked "Circ. File"
G. Clerk puts rubber bands around the six groups and
   gives them to the supervisor along with the drawer
   slip.

III. Catalog Department
   A. Clerk obtains from supervisor the groups of cards
      marked "See Official Catalog," groups of cards
      marked "See Check List," or groups of cards mark-
      ed "See Current Check List."
   B. Clerk alphabetizes the cards by groups.
   C. Clerk goes to Catalog Department.
   D. Clerk checks cards in the appropriate catalog.
      1. With blue ball-point pen writes down in the allot-
         ted space the entries that are missing when the

54

catalog entry is compared with the information from the books on the shelves and the books that are in circulation

    2. Checks box corresponding to "Catalog Department"

    3. If no books are missing and no other problems exist, checks "O. K."

E. Clerk sorts cards into three classes.

    1. Cards that are "O. K."

    2. Cards that are "Snags"

    3. All other cards

F. Clerk reports to supervisor.

IV. Second Shelf and Circulation Checks

A. Clerk holds cards 4-7 days.

B. Clerk takes suspected missing cards to shelves.

    1. Hunts for books

       a. Found: marks "O. K." and "2nd Shelf"

       b. Missing: marks "2nd Shelf"

C. Clerk sorts out "O. K." cards.

D. Clerk takes remaining cards to circulation file.

    1. Checks circulation slips for checked out books

       a. Checked out in file: slashes out entries and checks "2nd Circ."

       b. No record: checks "2nd Circ."

       c. If all entries accounted for: checks "O. K."

E. Clerk sorts out all "O. K." cards, groups remaining cards as "Missing".

F. Clerk reports to supervisor for instructions.

This process is summarized in the Inventory Flow Chart.

Three examples are given in Appendix A.

Determination of Time to Complete an Inventory

The first step required in the calculation of the total time to complete an inventory of the General Library was the determination of the number of General Library (GL) shelf list cards.

A count of the number of drawers for each Library of Congress classification was made. Ten percent of the drawers in each

Inventory Flow Chart

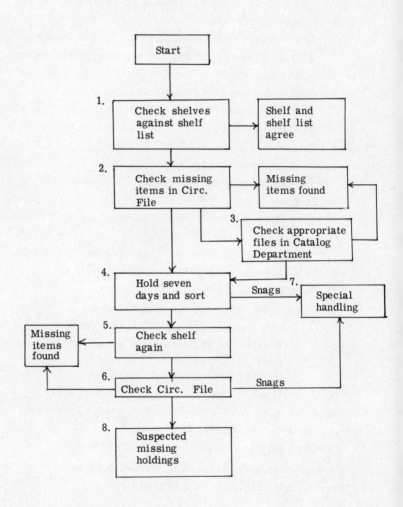

classification were randomly sampled in order to determine the average number of inches of cards per drawer and the percent of "GL" cards per drawer. It is generally accepted by the Catalog Department that there are 100 shelf list cards per inch.

A time study was conducted to determine the incremental times of the elements in each procedure. The average percentage of inventory cards processed in each function of the procedure was recorded for use in calculating the total time to complete the inventory. An average percentage for the whole shelf list is used instead of a separate percentage for each classification because of the ease of collecting the information and its low cost. More drawers and cards would have to be sampled to determine individual percentages than to use one percentage to represent the whole shelf list. This also would take more effort and would cost more. The difference of these representative percentages over the individual percentages is statistically very minor. In other words, the results are neither more nor less accurate, but are easier and less costly to obtain. The findings of the time study are presented below.

Shelf List Data

L. C. classifications	Total no. of drawers	Ave. no. cards per drawer	Total no. of cards	%G. L. cards	Total no. of G. L. cards
A	8.7	970	8,439	96 %	8,101
B	78.4	975	76,440	91.3%	70,566
C	8.6	1020	8,772	88.4%	7,754
D	98.6	1075	105,995	93.7%	99,317
E	20.9	1100	22,990	76.5%	17,587
F	20.2	1080	21,816	82 %	17,889
G	18.4	1100	20,240	64 %	12,954
H	142.8	1000	142,800	70 %	99,960
J	41.2	1010	41,612	59.5%	24,759
L	38.2	1060	40,492	66 %	26,725
N	41.8	965	40,337	50.3%	20,290
P	81.2	860	69,832	18.2%	12,709
Q	152.2	720	109,584	24.4%	26,738
R	36.8	750	27,600	10 %	2,760
S	31.2	670	20,904	58.5%	12,229
T	77.8	650	50,570	27 %	13,654
U	7.2	860	6,192	75 %	4,644
V	4.3	900	3,870	50 %	1,935
Z	44.4	850	37,740	60 %	22,644
	952.9		856,225		503,215
Dewey Classification	204	970	198,000	-	-

Breakdown of Inventory Cards into Functions

Library of Congress Classification

(1) Shelf Reading Phase

    (A) 16.9% of GL cards must have inventory cards filled out for further processing.

    (B) .0166 team-min./shelf-list card to distinguish GL shelf list cards.

    (C) .1 team-min/GL card for the card reader to read the call number and for the shelf searcher to answer.

    (D) .5 team-min./GL card to fill out an inventory card

(2) Preliminary Circulation File Check

    (A) 40% of the inventory cards are filled out or okayed by first circulation file check.

    (B) 41.8% of the inventory cards filled out are suspected missing after the first circulation check.

    (C) 10% of the inventory cards are checked as snags.

    (D) 6.8% of the inventory cards are marked "See the Check List".

    (E) 1.4% of the inventory cards are marked "See Official Catalog".

    (F) .25 man-min/card to process inventory cards in circulation file

(3) Catalog Searching Activity

    (A) 90% of those marked "See Official Catalog" are okayed.

    (B) 9.3% of those marked "See Official Catalog" were snags.

    (C) .7% of those marked "See Official Catalog" were suspected missing.

    (D) 80% of those marked "See Check List" were okayed.

    (E) 5% of those marked "See Check List" were snags.

    (F) 15% of those marked "See Check List" were suspected missing.

    (G) 1.7 man-min/card to process inventory cards in the Official Catalog.

    (H) 2.1 man-min/card to process inventory cards in the check list.

(4) Second Shelf Check

    (A) . 27 man-min/card to do second shelf check.

    (B) 80% still are missing after second shelf check.

    (C) 20% are okayed after second shelf check.

(5) Second Circulation File Check

    (A) . 25 man-min/card to process inventory cards in circulation file.

    (B) 59% of inventory cards are still "Suspected Missing".

    (C) 2% of inventory cards are checked as snags.

    (D) 39% of inventory cards are okayed.

Dewey Classification

(1) Shelf Reading Phase

    (A) 35% of shelf list cards have to have an inventory card filled out for further processing.

    (B) . 1 team-min./GL card for the card reader to read the call number and for the shelf searcher to answer.

    (C) . 5 team-min./GL card to fill out an inventory card.

(2) Preliminary Circulation File Check

    (A) 50% of inventory cards are okayed by first circulation check.

    (B) 20% of inventory cards are checked as snags.

    (C) . 5 team-min./GL card to fill out an inventory card.

(2) Preliminary Circulation File Check

    (A) 50% of inventory cards are okayed by first circulation check.

    (B) 20% of inventory cards are checked as snags.

    (C) 19. 8% of inventory cards are suspected missing.

    (D) 10. 2% of inventory cards are marked "See Official Catalog" or "See Check List".

    (E) . 25 man-min./card to process inventory cards in circulation file.

(3) Catalog Searching Activity

    (A) 1% of inventory cards are okayed.

    (B) 99% of inventory cards are suspected missing.

    (C) 1. 7 man-min./card to process cards in catalog department.

(4) Second Shelf Check

    (A) 81% are still suspected missing.

   (B) 19% are okayed.

   (C) .27 man-min./card to do second shelf check.

 (5) Second Circulation File Check

   (A) 59% are still "Suspected Missing".

   (B) 2% are marked "Snags".

   (C) 39% are okayed.

   (D) .25 man-min./card to do second circulation file check.

Calculation of the Number of Snags and Books that are Suspected Missing

LC Classification

  I. 85,000 inventory cards are filled out during the shelf-reading phase.

  II. (41.8%) (85,000) = 35,500 cards are suspected missing after first circulation file check.

     (10%) (85,000) = 8,500 cards are checked as snags.

     (6.8%) (85,000) = 5,780 cards are marked "See Check List".

     (1.4%) (85,000) = 1,190 cards are marked "See Official Catalog".

  III. (9.3%) (1,190) = 111 cards are snags after processing in the official catalog.

     (.7%) (1,190) = 8 cards are suspected missing after processing in the official catalog.

     (5%) (5,780) = 289 cards are snags after processing in the check list

     (15%) (5,780) = 867 cards are suspected missing after processing in the check list.

  IV. 35,500 + 8 + 867 = 36,375 cards will be processed during the second shelf check.

     (80%) (36,375) = 29,100 cards are still suspected missing after second shelf check.

  V. (59%) (29,100) = 17,200 cards are suspected missing after second circulation file check.

     (2%) (29,100) = 582 cards are snags after second circulation file check.

  VI. Totals

A. 17, 200 cards reflects the number of books that have a high probability of being missing from the library.

B. 8, 500 + 289 + 111 + 582 = 9, 482 cards are checked as snags and need further processing.

Dewey Classification

I. 69, 300 inventory cards are filled out during the shelf-reading phase.

II. (20%) (69, 300) = 13, 860 cards are checked as snags after the first circulation file check.

(19. 8%) (69, 300) = 13, 700 cards are suspected missing after the first circulation file check.

(10. 2%) (69, 300) = 7,070 cards are marked "See Official Catalog" or "See Check List".

III. (99%) (7, 070) = 7,000 cards are suspected missing after processing in the Catalog Department.

IV. 13, 700 + 7, 000 = 20, 700 cards are processed during the second shelf check.

(81%) (20, 700) = 16, 770 cards are still suspected missing after the second shelf check.

V. (59%) (16, 770) = 9, 900 cards are suspected missing after the second circulation file check.

(2%) (16, 770) = 335 cards are snags after the second circulation file check.

VI. Totals

A. 9, 900 cards reflect the number of books that have a high probability of being missing from the library.

B. 13, 860 + 335 = 14, 195 cards are checked as snags and need further processing.

Determination of Actual Time

To demonstrate the procedure used for determining the actual time to complete an inventory, some sample calculations will be presented. The key operation in terms of total time and complexity is the comparison of the shelf list cards with corresponding books on the shelves. The number of days to complete the operation is calculated first and the number of men needed for the other operations

61

is based on this number. As an example, assume that five two-man
teams are available to do the shelf list operation. The LC classification will be considered first. It was shown that it would take 107,022
team-minutes to complete the shelf list check. Applying a five percent allowance for each factor (fatigue, personal allowance, and non-
incentive work) to the time gives:

$$(.15) \ (107,022 \ \text{team-min.}) = 16,053 \ \text{team-min.}$$

Total adjusted time = $107,022 + 16,053 = 123,075$ team-min.

Since five teams would be working simultaneously, we divided by the
number of teams (5 teams):

$$\frac{123,092 \ \text{team-min.}}{5 \ \text{teams}} = 24,618 \ \text{minutes}$$

Converting to working days gives:

$$(24,618 \ \text{min.}) \ \frac{(1 \ \text{hr.})}{(60 \ \text{min.})} \frac{(1 \ \text{day})}{(8 \ \text{hr.})} = 51 \ \text{days}$$

During the same day of the shelf reading procedure, the inventory
control cards can be checked in the circulation file. The total unad-
justed production time to check the inventory control cards in the
circulation file was calculated to be 21,243 man-minutes. The adjusted production time is as follows:

$$(1.15) \ (21,250 \ \text{man-min.}) = 24,429 \ \text{man-min.} \quad \text{required for the}$$
$$\text{first circulation check.}$$

Converting to man-days:

$$(24,429 \ \text{man-min.}) \ \frac{(1 \ \text{hr.})}{(60 \text{min.})} \frac{(1 \ \text{day})}{(8 \ \text{hrs.})} = 51 \ \text{man-days}$$

The number of men required to complete the circulation file check
in 51 days:

$$\frac{51 \ \text{man-days}}{51 \ \text{days}} = 1 \ \text{man}$$

In other words, one man is required to work continuously for 51
days to complete the required inventory procedure in the circulation
file. A similar calculation for work in the cataloging department follows:

$$(1.15) \ (14,150 \ \text{man-min.}) = 16,152 \ \text{man-min}$$

Converted to man-days:

$$(16,152 \ \text{man-min.}) \ \frac{(1 \ \text{hr.})}{(60 \ \text{min.})} \frac{(1 \ \text{day})}{(8 \ \text{hr.})} = 34 \ \text{man-days}$$

The number of men required to complete the circulation file work in 34 man-days is $= \dfrac{34 \text{ man-days}}{51 \text{ days}} = .67$ men

Following the same calculation procedure, the results for the second shelf check and the second circulation file check were:

.47 men for the second shelf check

.35 men for the second circulation file check

The total number of employees required for completion of the LC classification in 51 working days is found as follows:

10 men (5 teams) - shelf list check

1 man - first circulation file check

.67 men - catalog-department check

.47 men - second shelf check

.35 men - second circulation file check

12.49 = 13 men

This shows that 13 men need to be hired to work for 51 days to complete an inventory of the LC classifications. Although it appears that the library would be paying for one-half of a man who does no work, in reality there will be times when there is extra work to be done because of a temporary shortage of workers, etc..

At least two supervisors would be required for the 13 man work crew. One supervisor would logically be assigned to take care of the five shelf reading teams. The other would oversee the remaining inventory activities. Total supervisory time was not included, since these people are needed 100% of the time, regardless of the amount of work done by the work crew. It is also recommended that a messenger be assigned to the inventory crew to replace finished drawers and bring to the shelf readers new drawers from the Catalog Department. He could also be used to take the inventory cards from one supervisor to another and to run other assorted errands. It should be recognized that in computing the numbers of days to complete the inventory, it was assumed that the teams were fully trained and were performing at normal peak efficiency.

The corresponding calculations for the Dewey section are as follows:

63

Systems Analysis in a University Library

Using 5 teams

$$\frac{(1.15)\ (54,450\ \text{team-min.})\ \frac{(1\ \text{hr.})}{60\ \text{min.}}\ \frac{(1\ \text{day})}{8\ \text{hr.}}}{\dfrac{\text{shelf reading}}{5\ \text{teams}}} = 26.1\ \text{days}$$

First Circulation File Check

$$\frac{(1.15)\ (17,325\ \text{man-min.})\ \frac{(1\ \text{hr.})}{60\ \text{min.}}\ \frac{(1\ \text{day})}{8\ \text{hr.}}}{26.1\ \text{days}} = 1.59\ \text{men}$$

Catalog Check

$$\frac{(1.15)\ (12,000\ \text{man-min.})\ \frac{(1\ \text{hr.})}{60\ \text{min.}}\ \frac{(1\ \text{day})}{8\ \text{hrs.}}}{26.1\ \text{days}} = 1.10\ \text{men}$$

Second Shelf List

$$\frac{(1.15)\ (5,580\ \text{man-min.})\ \frac{(1\ \text{hr.})}{60\ \text{min.}}\ \frac{(1\ \text{day})}{8\ \text{hr.}}}{26.1\ \text{days}} = .51\ \text{men}$$

Second Circulation File Check

$$\frac{(1.15)\ (4,188\ \text{man-min.})\ \frac{(1\ \text{hr.})}{60\ \text{min.}}\ \frac{(1\ \text{day})}{8\ \text{hrs.}}}{26.1\ \text{days}} = .38\ \text{men}$$

Total number of employees required to complete the Dewey Classifications in 28 days:

10 men (5 teams)	shelf list check
1.59 men	1st circulation file check
1.10 men	catalog check
.51 men	second shelf check
.38 men	2nd circulation file check
13.58 = 14 men	

This calculation shows that it is necessary to work 14 men for a period of 28 days to complete an inventory of the Dewey Classification.

Problem Areas

1. Training Problems

On the basis of the findings of this study, there is little doubt that the inventory procedures, with the exception of the follow-up activities, could be taught with relative ease to university students. Most procedures could be taught with a day of on-the-job instruction, assuming some prior orientation regarding the general aspects of the inventory procedure.

64

A question arises as to the advisability of using high school students as workers on the inventory teams. The only way of accurately testing this hypothesis is to conduct a small pilot training program with high school students and to evaluate the results.

2. Shelf Checking

It is desirable to use separate groups of shelf checking teams to read the LG and Dewey classifications. The call numbers in each of the two sections must be interpreted differently and the order of appearance of books on the shelves is different in each of the sections, although the basic inventory procedures are not different for the two classifications. Separation of the work force into two groups could eliminate much confusion and thus reduce the possibility of errors. Interpretation of the shelf list card formats would be easier if teams were not shifted from one section to another.

3. Shelf Order

One of the problems which was anticipated in conducting the inventory was dealing with misshelved books. Before beginning the study it was thought that a prior shelf reading and ordering activity might be required before the stack checks. The study indicated that shelf order is adequate. The number of misshelved books found did not interfere in any significant way with the shelf checks.

4. Interference with Re-shelving

The proposed inventory procedure does not interfere with present shelving activities in the stacks. Any books which are suspected missing as a result of a first shelf and circulation check, but are in the process of being returned to the shelves, are caught by the second shelf and circulation checks.

5. Processing "Book Dummies"

Whenever a "dummy" is encountered on the shelf, an inventory card is prepared as outlined in the shelf-checking procedure described above. Clearly, the presence of a "dummy" on the shelf does not imply that the actual volumes or copies of the present holdings represented are present, correctly shelved, and identified in the folio cases. It is impractical to track down these entries as they occur on the shelves. The process of searching the folio cases is time-consuming, and the books must be handled with care since many are in a fragile condition.

It is recommended that inventory control cards marked "Dummy" routing designations be separated from the other cards immediately after the first circulation check, and filed for separate processing at a later date.

6. Verification of Missing Entries

It is theoretically desirable to have every holding verified and all records cross-checked. For purposes of this inventory, the fact that a book is charged out in the circulation file is considered to be sufficient proof that the library still has control of the volume. Errors which do exist in these files will, in most cases, be corrected by other procedures.

7. Prolific Authors

It was suggested that the occurrence of prolific authors in the official catalog, such as John Milton, might not have been reflected in the sample inventory. It was found that the sample did include a significant number of prolific authors.

Conclusions

One concludes from the time study that the problems which would be encountered in the course of conducting an inventory of the General Library are not insurmountable and can be handled by the procedures developed in this report, assuming competent supervision of the work force and the close cooperation of affected departments. The study indicated that conducting the inventory over a relatively long span of time using a specially trained inventory team comprised of part-time university students was more effective. This has the advantage of making supervision easier, and it also lessens interference with library operations. Also, a smaller work force is required and greater accuracy is realized through the continuing improvement of work performance gained through experience.

The inventory system proposed in this report has been designed to permit employment of relatively inexperienced workers. This objective has been accomplished by reducing the number of alternative choices to be made at any given point in the process. However, the success of the inventory will rest with the supervisors.

The most important job of the supervisors will be answering questions and resolving the minor procedural problems which are likely to arise in the course of the inventory. As a part of their responsibility, they should periodically make checks on the accuracy of work done by the people in their charge. Close supervision by competent personnel would make possible on-the-job training without reducing total inventory accuracy and effectiveness markedly. This would also reduce the need for initial training and its associated non-productive costs. However, this approach does not eliminate the need for basic job orientation by written instructions and oral explanations prior to beginning actual work.

Another important point to remember, which also affects the success of an inventory, is the preparation of the library facilities prior to conducting the inventory. Pre-planning would be required of the library staff in each department affected by the inventory to insure the smooth coordination of necessary activities. Some additional equipment would have to be procured or purchased, especially if a large-scale operation was attempted.

The procedures outlined earlier will generate an estimated 17,200 inventory cards which reflect the number of books classified according to the Library of Congress system that have a high probability of being missing from the library. At the same time 9,482 cards will be generated that are checked as snags and require special handling. No estimates of the time to process these cards was made because of the uncertainty of the procedures involved in handling them and because of the expected high variability of the individual processing times. In the Dewey classifications 9,900 cards will have a high probability of being missing and 14,195 cards will be checked as snags.

A special notice should be paid to the section entitled "Determination of Actual Time." Notice that it was assumed that the five two-man teams are available to do the shelf list operation. The estimate of 51 days for the LC Classifications revolves around this assumption. Therefore, employing a different number of two-man teams will change the number of days to complete the inventory.

Systems Analysis in a University Library

This section was presented to show the calculations necessary to determine the length of the inventory given the number of two-man teams.

Final Comments

A review of the findings of this study has raised several important questions.

It appears that the sample on which the calculations were based did not include a representative number of serials. Further, the sample on which the serial processing times were based did not include enough difficult-to-process serials. The authors now believe that serials will have to be handled separately from the rest of the inventory by workers with considerable bibliographic skill.

Another question concerns the great amount of follow-up work which will be generated by an inventory. There will be 50,777 items which require further attention. Of these 27,100 will be books which are suspected missing. These will have to be evaluated by librarians to determine if they should be replaced. The other 23,677 will be items with difficult-to-interpret records and will have to be dealt with by skilled personnel. One cannot say whether the expense of processing these items will be offset by improved user service and reduced searching and catalog-maintenance costs.

At this time the most workable alternative seems to be partial inventories of selected sections. Hopefully this would provide the library with a better understanding of the costs and advantages of a large scale inventory.

Appendix A
Examples of Filled-out Control Cards

Example 1

GB 1278 R59 A77	Arocena, C.		Off. Cat.	
			Checklist	
	Lack on shelf	[X] 1, 2/1	Cur. Cklst	
			No Card	
		2, 3/2	Mislabeled	
	Have on shelf	[ ]	Dummy	
	Missing Circ. Record / Circ. Record		Snag	
			Circ. File	
			Cat. Dept.	
			2nd Shelf	
			2nd Circ.	
			O. K.	

Step 1:

This card indicates that copy 1 and copy 2 of volume 1, and copy 2 and copy 3 of volume 2 were not on the shelf at the time of the shelf list reading.

GB 1278 R59 A77	Arocena, C.		Off. Cat.	
			Checklist	
	Lack on shelf	[X] 1, 1/1	Cur. Cklst	
			No Card	
		1, 3/2	Mislabeled	
	Have on shelf	[ ]	Dummy	
	Missing Circ. Record / Circ. Record		Snag	
			Circ. File	X
			Cat. Dept.	
			2nd Shelf	
			2nd Circ.	
			O. K.	

Step 2:

The card now indicates that copy 1 of volume 1 and copy 3 of volume 2 are suspected missing. It also shows that copy 2 of volume 1 and copy 2 of volume 2 were in circulation.

GB 1278 R59 A77	Arocena, C.		Off. Cat.	
			Checklist	
	Lack on shelf	[X] 1, 1/1	Cur. Cklst	
			No Card	
		1, 1/2	Mislabeled	
	Have on shelf	[ ]	Dummy	
	Missing Circ. Record / Circ. Record		Snag	
			Circ. File	X
			Cat. Dept.	
			2nd Shelf	X
			2nd Circ.	
			O. K.	

Step 3:

During the second shelf check copy 3 of volume 2 was found. The card shows that copy 1 of volume 1 is still unaccounted for.

GB 1278 R59 A77	Arocena, C.			Off. Cat.	
				Checklist	
	Lack on shelf	[X]	1, 1/1	Cur. Cklst	
				No Card	
	Have on shelf		1, 1/2	Mislabeled	
				Dummy	
	Missing Circ. Record / Circ. Record			Snag	
				Circ. File	X
				Cat. Dept.	
				2nd Shelf	X
				2nd Circ.	X
				O. K.	

Step 4:
The card indicates that copy 1 of volume 1 is still unaccounted for, since no record could be found in the circulation file.

Example 2

QD 22 S68 A3	Soddy, F.			Off. Cat.	X
				Checklist	
	Lack on shelf		1-10/1, 1-7/2	Cur. Cklst	
				No Card	
	Have on shelf	[X]	1/3	Mislabeled	
				Dummy	
	Missing Circ. Record / Circ. Record			Snag	
				Circ. File	
				Cat. Dept.	
				2nd Shelf	
				2nd Circ.	
				O. K.	

Step 1:
During the shelf list reading, the shelf list card said to see the offical catalog in order to verify holdings. The volumes listed are those that are on the shelf.

QD 22 S68 A3	Soddy, F.			Off. Cat.	X
				Checklist	
	Lack on shelf		1-10/1, 1-7/2	Cur. Cklst	
				No Card	
	Have on shelf	[X]	1/3	Mislabeled	
				Dummy	
	Missing Circ. Record / Circ. Record	8, 9/2 2-4/3		Snag	
				Circ. File	X
				Cat. Dept.	
				2nd Shelf	
				2nd Circ.	
				O. K.	

Step 2:
The circulation file shows that copies 8 and 9 of volume 2 and copies 2, 3 and 4 of volume 3 are in circulation. This record is needed to determine missing holdings when the official catalog is consulted.

70

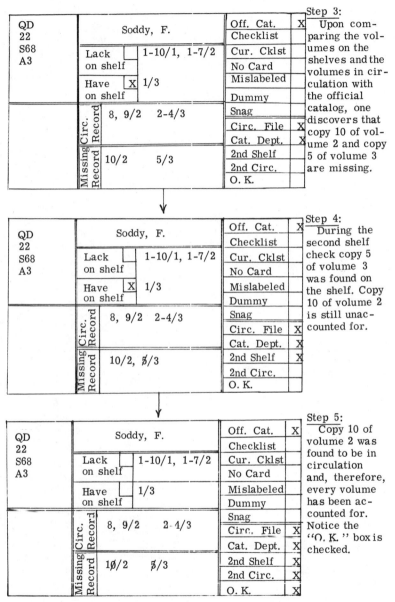

Step 3:
Upon comparing the volumes on the shelves and the volumes in circulation with the official catalog, one discovers that copy 10 of volume 2 and copy 5 of volume 3 are missing.

Step 4:
During the second shelf check copy 5 of volume 3 was found on the shelf. Copy 10 of volume 2 is still unaccounted for.

Step 5:
Copy 10 of volume 2 was found to be in circulation and, therefore, every volume has been accounted for. Notice the "O. K." box is checked.

Example 3

<table>
<tr><td rowspan="7">GB
468.89
G79
A3</td><td colspan="2">Great Barrier Reef</td><td>Off. Cat.</td><td></td></tr>
<tr><td></td><td></td><td>Checklist</td><td>X</td></tr>
</table>

Step 1:

GB 468.89 G79 A3	Great Barrier Reef		Off. Cat.	
			Checklist	X
	Lack on shelf	1/1-5	Cur. Cklst	
			No Card	
	Have on shelf	X	Mislabeled	
			Dummy	
	Missing Circ. Record / Circ. Record		Snag	
			Circ. File	
			Cat. Dept.	
			2nd Shelf	
			2nd Circ.	
			O. K.	

Step 1: The shelf list card said to see the check list for official holdings. Therefore, the volumes on the shelf were recorded. There is 1 copy of 5 volumes on the shelf.

GB 468.89 G79 A3	Great Barrier Reef		Off. Cat.	
			Checklist	X
	Lack on shelf	1/1-5	Cur. Cklst	
			No Card	
	Have on shelf	X	Mislabeled	
			Dummy	
	Missing Circ. Record / Circ. Record — No Record		Snag	
			Circ. File	X
			Cat. Dept.	
			2nd Shelf	
			2nd Circ.	
			O. K.	

Step 2: The circulation file showed no volumes were checked out.

GB 468.89 G79 A3	Great Barrier Reef		Off. Cat.	
			Checklist	X
	Lack on shelf	1/1-5	Cur. Cklst	
			No Card	
	Have on shelf	X	Mislabeled	
			Dummy	
No card in check list	Missing Circ. Record / Circ. Record — No Record		Snag	X
			Circ. File	X
			Cat. Dept.	X
			2nd Shelf	
			2nd Circ.	
			O. K.	

Step 4: As the card indicates, no card could be found in the check list. This card now becomes a snag needing special handling at some later date.

72

Appendix B
Calculation of Total Time - L. C. Classification

1. Shelf Reading Phase

A) (16.9%) (503, 215 G. L. Cards) = 85,000 inventory cards to be filled out

B) $[\frac{.0166 \text{ team-min.}}{\text{shelf list card}}]$ (856, 225 shelf list cards) = 14, 200 team-min. to distinguish GL shelf list cards

C) $[\frac{.1 \text{ team-min.}}{\text{GL Card}}]$ (503, 215 G. L. cards) = 50, 322 team-min. to read call number and receive an answer

D) $[\frac{.5 \text{ team-min.}}{\text{Gl Card}}]$ (85, 000 inventory cards) = 42, 500 team-min. to fill out inventory cards

E) Total time to complete shelf reading phase
$[\frac{2 \text{ men}}{\text{team}}]$ (107, 022 team-min.) = 214, 044 man-min.

2. Preliminary Circulation File Check

a) $[\frac{.25 \text{ man-min.}}{\text{card}}]$ (85, 000 inventory cards) = 21, 250 man-min. to process inventory cards in circulation file

b) Total time to complete preliminary circulation file check = 21, 250 man-min.

3. Catalog Searching Activity

A) (6.8%) (85, 000) = 5, 780 inventory cards to be processed in the check list

B) (5, 780 cards) $[\frac{2.1 \text{ man-min.}}{\text{card}}]$ = 12, 130 man-min. to process cards in the check list

C) (1.4%) (85, 000) = 1, 190 inventory cards to be processed in the official catalog

D) (1, 190 cards) $[\frac{1.7 \text{ man-min.}}{\text{card}}]$ = 2, 020 man-min. to process cards in the official catalog

E) Total time to complete catalog searching activity
12, 130 + 2, 020 = 14, 150 man-min.

4. Second Shelf Check

A) (.7%) (1, 190 cards) = 8 cards to be processed further after official catalog check

B) (15%) (5, 780) = 867 cards to be processed further after check list check

    C) (41.8%) $(85,000)$ = 35,600 cards suspected missing after first circulation check

    D) $8 + 867 + 35,600 = 36,375$ cards for further processing

    E) (36,375 cards) $\left[.27 \frac{\text{man-min.}}{\text{card}} \right] = 9,860$ man-min. to do second shelf check

    F) Total time to complete the second shelf check = 9,860 man-min.

5. Second Circulation File Check

    A) (80%) $(36,375)$ = 29,100 cards to be processed during second circulation check

    B) $\left[.25 \frac{\text{man-min.}}{\text{card}} \right]$ (29,100 cards) = 7,350 man-min.

    C) Total time to complete second circulation file check = 7,350 man-min.

    Total Time - L. C. Classification

1. Stacks Operations	214,044	man-min.
2. First Circulation File Check	21,250	man-min.
3. Catalog Department Check	14,150	man-min.
4. Second Shelf Check	9,860	man-min.
5. Second Circulation File Check	7,350	man-min.
	266,654	man-min.

$\left[\frac{1 \text{ hr.}}{60 \text{ min.}} \right]$ (266,654 man-min.) = 4,450 man-hrs.

The total time to complete inventory procedures in the L. C. Classification is 4,450 man-hrs.

    Calculation of Total Time - Dewey Classification

1. Shelf Reading Phase

    A) (35%) (198,000 shelf list cards) = 69,300 inventory cards to be filled out

    B) $\left[.1 \frac{\text{team-min.}}{\text{card}} \right]$ (198,000 cards) = 19,800 team-min. to read call number and receive an answer

    C) $\left[.5 \frac{\text{team-min.}}{\text{card}} \right]$ (69,300 cards) = 34,650 team-min. to fill out inventory cards

    D) Total time to complete shelf reading phase

    $(19,800 + 34,650) = 54,450$ team-min.

    (54,450 team-min) $\left[2 \frac{\text{men}}{\text{team}} \right]$ = 108,900 man-min.

74

2. First Circulation File Check

   A) $[.25 \frac{\text{man-min.}}{\text{card}}]$ (69, 300 cards) = 17, 325 man-min.

   B) Total time to complete first circulation file check 17, 325

           man-min.

3. Catalog Searching Activity

   A) (10. 2%) (69, 300 cards) = 7, 070 cards to process in Catalog

           Department

   B) (7, 070 cards) $[1.7 \frac{\text{man-min.}}{\text{card}}]$ = 12, 000 man-min.

   C) Total time to complete card catalog searching activity =

           12, 000 man-min.

4. Second Shelf Check

   A) (99%) (7, 070) = 7000 cards for further processing after Cata-

           log Department check

   B) (19. 8%) (69, 300) = 13, 700 cards for further processing after

           the first circulation file check

   C) 7,000 + 13,700 = 20, 700 cards for further processing

   D) $[.27 \frac{\text{man-min.}}{\text{card}}]$ (20, 700 cards) = 5, 580 man-min.

   E) Total time to complete second shelf check = 5, 580 man-min.

5. Second Circulation File Check

   A) (81%) (20, 200) = 16, 750 cards to be processed during second

           circulation check

   B) $[.25 \frac{\text{man-min.}}{\text{card}}]$ (16, 750 cards) = 4, 188 man-min.

   C) Total time to complete second circulation file check = 4, 188

           man-min.

Total Time - Dewey Classification

1. Stacks Operation	108, 900 man-min.
2. First Circulation File Check	17, 325 man-min.
3. Catalog Department Check	12, 000 man-min.
4. Second Shelf Check	5, 580 man-min.
5. Second Circulation File Check	4, 188 man-min.
	147, 993 man-min.

$[\frac{1 \text{ hr.}}{60 \text{ min.}}]$ (147, 993 man-min.) = 2, 470 man-hrs.

The total time to complete inventory procedures in the Dewey Classifi-

           cation is 2, 470 man-hrs.

Analysis of Book Reshelving

By: H. L. Benford, B. R. Burkhalter, G. C. Ehrnstrum, L. L. Hoag

Introduction

It is estimated that the University of Michigan General Library contains about 1,400,000 volumes, and has an annual circulation of approximately 200,000 books. The Stacks Section of the Circulation Department is responsible for reshelving all books returned from outside circulation, and all other volumes taken from shelves but not removed from the library. A study of the Stacks Section operation was undertaken because a significant delay existed between the time books were returned and the actual placement of books back on the shelves. In addition, it was believed that books underwent an excessive number of handling operations in this sorting-reshelving process. In other words, the study objective was to reduce the time and cost of getting the books back on the shelf.

An analysis of the existing system determined the average reshelving delay to be 3 to 4 days and the average reshelving cost to be 22¢. It is estimated that the four recommendations made as a result of this study would reduce the reshelving delay to approximately one day and the reshelving cost to approximately 16¢ per volume reshelved. The estimated annual savings of $12,270 (existing system annual cost = $43,350; proposed system annual cost = $31,080) could be achieved with a change-over investment of $275.

More specifically:

1. All books returned by 6:00 p.m. on any given day would be reshelved before normal hours of operation on the next working day.

2. Methods improvements in the following areas would result in a reduction of 10,300 man-hours per year in the Stacks Section.

	Man-hour Savings/Year
a) Collection of books from drop boxes	901
b) Relayout of sorting room	496

76

c) Reassignment of personnel   8,903

total ▪   10,300

In addition, approximately 340 more man-hours annually would be made available to the Circulation Department.

Existing System

Areas included in the investigation of the General Library Stacks Section were the book-handling process and the work-scheduling process.

1. Book-handling Process - This operation accomplishes the reshelving of volumes returned from circulation, or removed from the shelves but remaining in the library.

    a. Volumes Returned from Circulation - The receiving points for these books are the four large mail boxes, hereafter called drop boxes, located outside the library building, and the receiving desk located in the Circulation Department. The procedure followed in drop-box collection and the time to complete this operation are below.

Procedure:

1. Pick up two canvas bags in the Stacks Section
2. Pick up keys to drop box.
3. Walk to drop boxes in the front of the library with the bags and keys.
4. Unlock one of the boxes.
5. Remove the books from the box and place them in one of the canvas bags.
6. Continue unloading the boxes until both canvas bags are full.
7. Return to the Stacks Section with the filled canvas bags.
8. Leave the filled canvas bags there and pick up two empty ones.
9. Repeat steps 3 through 8 until all the books have been taken from the drop boxes.
10. Return the keys.

Time:

The boxes are emptied 12 times a day and each such collection requires 3 separate trips. Thus, 36 trips per day are made. The

77

average walking time per trip (bag empty, going out, full coming back) was determined to be 5.0 minutes. The average drop box unloading time per trip (fill two bags) was determined to be 2.67 minutes. The annual man-hours spent on this operation can be calculated as:

$$(5.0 + 2.67) \frac{\text{min.}}{\text{trip}} \times 36 \frac{\text{trips}}{\text{day}} \times 340 \frac{\text{days}}{\text{year}} \times \frac{1 \text{ hrs.}}{60 \text{ min.}} = 1,565 \frac{\text{hrs.}}{\text{year}}$$

All books collected from drop boxes and the circulation desk are taken to the stackroom located in the basement where each volume is discharged to a holding area. When two shelves are full in this area, the carbon slips from each book are sent to the circulation desk and matched with the original charge slips. The Circulation Department personnel then go to the stackroom, withdraw "hold" books from the holding area, and release the remaining books on the two shelves for further processing. The delay in this holding area was observed to be one to four days. After release, books are moved by carts to the sorting area where they are off-loaded to shelves arranged according to floor. Next, books are on-loaded to carts by call number, and taken to their respective floors on a time-scheduled basis. The present book-handling process in the stackroom involves four book-handlings and two in-process delays. See below for details of the man-hours expended annually for book movement in the holding-sorting-loading area.

A. Truck Movement

    1. Door to discharging area
       (53 ft. x 4,280 moves per year)   = 226,840 ft.

    2. Hold to sorting area
       (42 ft. x 2,630 moves per year)   = 110,460 ft.

    3. Sorting to hold area
       (15 ft. x 2,630 moves per year)   = <u>39,450</u> ft.

       Total distance moved per year   = 376,750 ft. per yr.

    4. Rate of movement
       (determined by testing)   = 9,480 ft./man-hr.

       Total annual time   = $\frac{376,750}{9,480 \text{ ft./man-hrs.}}$ = 39.4 man-hours

B. Individual Book Movement

    1. Average distance moved per book = 6-1/4 ft.

2. Books sorted per year = 273,000
  Total distance moved per year = 6 1/4 x 273,000 = 1,706,250 ft.

3. Rate of movement
  (determined by observation) = 12,480 ft. per man-hour
  Total annual time = $\dfrac{1,706,250}{12,480}$ = 137 man-hours

C. Book Handling

  1. Each book is handled four times

  2. Books handled per year = 198,000

  3. Time per handling
    (determined by testing) = 3-1/2 seconds per handling
    Total annual time = $\dfrac{198,000 \times 4 \times 3\text{-}1/2}{3,600}$ = 770 man-hours

D. Total Annual Time = 39.4 + 137 + 770 = 946.4 man-hours

  b. Volumes Removed from Shelves but Remaining in the Library - The reshelving procedures for these books are determined by the area in which they are found. If volumes are near their proper shelves they are reshelved immediately. Volumes located on the correct floor but not near their proper shelves are placed on temporary shelves and reshelved at a later time. Books which have been displaced to other floors are taken by carts to the stackroom and enter the sorting process described above. Books found in the reading room are also returned to the stackroom for sorting.

  2. Work-scheduling Process - Work scheduling in the existing system is done hourly by the supervisor or assistant supervisor. The scheduling operation entails checking the people working against personal qualifications and job requirements, and listing the jobs and workers on a sheet of paper which is then tacked to the bulletin board. This requires about 10-15 minutes per hour. Jobs which are scheduled include shelving, shelf-reading, picking up drop boxes, trading trucks, discharging, sorting, loading, distributing trucks, replacing light bulbs, picking up books from the outlying areas, the ranges, and the periodical reading rooms and the graduate reading rooms and tidying up these areas, searching overdues, taking care

79

of the folios, lettering, searching Interlibrary Loan requests, taking care of the display case, clearing temporary shelves, opening and closing the stacks, shifting, working at the annex, bringing the annex box from the Circulation Department, transferring new books, and training.

Proposed System

A careful analysis of the existing system indicated that corrective action in the areas of drop-box collection, holding-area procedures, stackroom layout, and personnel work-scheduling, would reduce the delay time and man-hour requirements for reshelving books.

1. <u>Drop Box Collection</u> - Cost savings can be obtained by changing the procedure for collecting books returned to the outside drop-boxes. Under the existing procedures, three separate trips must be made with the small book bags to completely empty all the drop-boxes. The proposed system is designed to enable the books to be collected in one trip. The small bags are replaced by large canvas mail bags which fit in the drop boxes. These bags can be removed from the boxes and replaced with empty ones when collections are made, thus eliminating the handling of books at the drop boxes. Since the full bags are too heavy to carry easily, a flat-bed cart will be used to transport them. This will enable all the drop-boxes to be emptied in one trip.

On the basis of experimentation, it was determined that each trip would take 9.8 man-minutes, 5.8 minutes traveling and 4.0 minutes exchanging empty bags for full ones. This produces a total annual time of:

$$(5.8 + 4.0) \; \frac{\text{min.}}{\text{trip}} \; x \; 12 \; \frac{\text{trips}}{\text{day}} \; x \; 340 \; \frac{\text{days}}{\text{year}} \; x \; \frac{1 \; \text{hr.}}{60 \; \text{min.}} = 664 \frac{\text{hrs.}}{\text{year}},$$ a savings

of 901 man-hours per year. Using an effective hourly cost of $1.19 (calculated using the procedure described in the "Memo on Effective Labor Costs"), the dollar value of the annual labor savings of the proposed system over the existing system is 901 x $1.19 = $1,072.

The question is whether or not the annual savings are sufficient to justify the investment needed to change over to the new system. This investment amounts to $175, calculated as follows:

    Cost of canvas bags (10 bags at $5.00 apiece)   = $50

    Flat-bed truck   = $75

    Labor cost to alter boxes to hold bags $50

                                   Total = $175

The pay-back period of the new investment is only 2 months, indicating that the change should be made.

2. <u>Hold Area Elimination</u> - The book-holding procedure appears to be the key delay in the reshelving process. It can vary from one to four days depending on how soon personnel from the Circulation Department find time to come to the Stacks Section and identify the hold books. As their work-load pressures build up, circulation personnel tend to put off this duty because it does not affect any of their other work. In effect, the Stacks Section is held accountable for returning the books to the shelves as quickly as possible, but does not have complete authority over the process; the Circulation Department holds part of this authority.

The intent of this proposal is to begin the sorting-loading process of all books returned to the stackroom immediately upon their arrival, without "holding" until released by Circulation Department personnel. This is possible if a copy of every hold slip is forwarded from the Circulation Department to the Stacks Section as soon as the slip is written, so that the hold file can be maintained in the Stacks Section. Then all incoming books are checked against the hold file by Stacks Section personnel before they are sent to the floors. The hold books can then be sent up to the Circulation Department while the other books are being taken to the stacks. In other words, the authority for searching for and pulling hold books is transferred to the Stacks Section so that the responsibility and authority rest in one place.

In view of the existing delays in the hold area, it is estimated that books will be reshelved two to three days sooner than by the existing system. In addition, it was observed that Circulation personnel average three trips to the Stacks Section per day for hold-book pickup under the existing system. This activity would be eliminated, saving one man-hour per day or 340 man-hours per year.

3. <u>Stackroom Layout</u> - Figure 1 shows representations of existing and proposed layouts of the book sorting area. Under the proposed layout, books are sorted onto shelves from the inside of the ''U'' and subsequently loaded onto carts from the outside of the ''U''. Thus, the sorting and loading operations can go on simultaneously without interferring with each other as they do in the existing system. In addition, the proposed layout has numerous other advantages:

    a) unidirectional book flow

    b) reduced walking distance

    c) increased number of simultaneous loading operations

    d) elimination of holding area

    e) reduction of number of book handlings to two

    f) adaptability to circulation growth (excess shelves - not shown in Figure 1)

By changing the layout, numerous procedures could be improved. The most important is the elimination of the hold area entirely; hold books are removed directly from the carts before they are sent to the stacks. All in all, the annual man-hour savings within the Stacks Section amount to 496. 2 man-hours. The details of the savings can be seen by comparing the man-hours associated with the existing system with the man-hours associated with the proposed system, shown below. There is a labor cost of approximately $100 to move the shelves into the proposed positions, compared to the annual savings of (496. 2 man-hours) x ($1. 19) = $590. 48.

Stack Room Book Movement and Handling Time - Proposed System

A. Truck Movement

    1. Door to discharging area
       (8 ft. x 4,280 moves per year)   = 34, 240 ft

    2. Discharge area to stacks
       (25 ft. x 2,630 moves per year)   = 65, 750 ft.

       Total distance moved per year = 99, 990 ft. per year

    3. Rate of movement   = 9, 480 ft. per man-hour

       Total annual time $= \dfrac{99,990}{9,480}$ = 10. 5 man-hours

Layout of Book Sorting Area

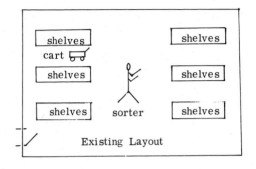

Existing Layout

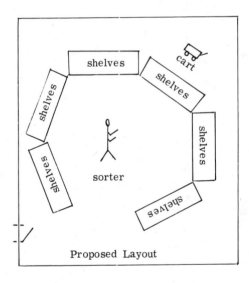

Proposed Layout

Analysis in a University Library

B. Individual Book Movement

    1. Average distance moved per book = 2 1/2 ft.

    2. Books sorted per year = 273,000

        Total distance moved per year = 2 1/2 x 273,000 = 682,500 ft.

    3. Rate of movement = 12,480 ft. per man-hour

$$\text{Total annual time} = \frac{682,500}{12,480} = 54.7 \text{ man-hours}$$

C. Book Handling

    1. Each book is handled twice.

    2. Books handled per year = 198,000.

    3. Time per handling = 3 1/2 seconds.

$$\text{Total annual time} = \frac{198,000 \times 2 \times 3\ 1/2}{3,600} = 385 \text{ man-hours}$$

D. Total Annual Time of Proposed System = 10.5 + 54.7 + 385 = 450.2 man-hours

    4. <u>Stack Personnel Work Schedule</u> - It was observed that excessive man-time was spent on picking up drop boxes, pulling and dating carbon slips, sorting, shelving, picking up books on the floors, and shelf-reading. Some of this excessive time would be eliminated by the above proposals, but lack of scheduling and standards also seem to be at fault. There seem to be two problems. First, the supervisor spends a great deal of time preparing and explaining work schedules each hour because many of the part-time employees only work for one hour stretches. When this is the case, a relatively large amount of time is spent at the beginning of each hour finding out what to do. Second, the work rate seems to be slow.

    The method of scheduling under the proposed system involves the supervisor's scheduling personnel for at least two hours at a time. In addition, the same work schedule is prepared for each week in the semester so that the supervisor would not have to develop new schedules for the personnel every day. He would check the jobs to be done during a time period, noting especially the required number of hours for shelving; he would check the workers' qualifications; and he would schedule them for two to four hours of work. (One hour work-spans would be eliminated so that less time is wasted due to unproductive time at the beginning and end of a work span. However, the success of this recommended change depends on the

84

library's ability to find students whose classes allow them to work two or more hours in a row.)

In order to increase the rate of work, production standards have been set for the tasks in question. This allows the supervisor to schedule work realistically and provides him with some control over the work being done. Time studies were taken and the following standards were obtained:

Task	Rate Per Man-Hour
Pick up drop-boxes, pull and date carbon slips, sort books onto shelves	142 books
Load onto book-carts and check for holds	190

The standard for shelving and shelf-reading was more difficult to obtain, but was finally set at 330 man-hours per week on the basis of experienced opinion. Figure 5 shows how the standards were obtained.

Based on the above standards, the total number of hours scheduled per day of the week are:

Sunday	Sunday	53 hours
	Monday	113
	Tuesday	98
	Wednesday	82
	Thursday	88
	Friday	82
	Saturday	52
	Total	568 hours

In addition to the allowance for absences and peak loads included in the above calculations, three hours on weekdays and two hours on weekend days are recommended as an additional allowance. This would bring the total to 587 hours per week. Applying this figure over the year (assuming 50% use during interim periods and 75% use during the summer session) an annual use of 26,100 hours is found. This represents a savings of 8,903 man-hours annually due to scheduling and the establishment of standards and a total of 10,300 hours below the 36,400 budgeted for the entire Stacks Section for the existing system. This figure, however, does not include hours required for major shifting operations, the frequency and extent of which usually cannot be predicted. Some allowance of time for these activities would be necessary.

85

Standard Time for Operations

I. Picking up bags from drop-boxes, pulling carbons, sorting

Task	Rate	Allowance*	Rate With Allowance
Picking up bags from drop-boxes	.131 min./book	(5%, 4%, 2%) = 11%	.146 min./book
Pull carbon slips	.150 min./book	(5%, 4%, 2%) = 11%	.166 min./book
Sort books onto shelves by floor	.038 min./book	(5%, 2%, 1%) = 8%	.041 min./book
Date carbon slips			10 minutes every hour

Total books/hour = $\dfrac{60 \text{ min./hr.} - 10 \text{ min./hr. (for drop-boxes)}}{(.146 + .166 + .041) \text{ min./book}}$ = 142 books/hour

II. Loading

Put books on truck by call number	.228 min./book	(5%, 4%, 2%) = 11	.253 min./book
Check hold slips	4 min./truck + 63 books/truck =		.064 min./book

Total books/hour = $\dfrac{60 \text{ min./hr.}}{(.253 + .064) \text{ min./book}}$ = 190 books/hour

III. Shelving and shelf-reading

Shelf-reading: On the basis of administrative experience and policy,
Shelving: On the basis of observation and administrative experience,
Average books shelved/week = 4,700 average circulation/week
+ 4,500 average left on tables/week

Average shelving time/week = $\dfrac{(4,700 + 4,500) \text{ books/week}}{60 \text{ books/hr.}}$ = 153 hrs./week

Allowance for absences and peak loads = 23 hrs./week

Total hours/week = (154 + 153 + 23) = 330 hours/week

* Allowance percentages are for personal, fatigue, and delay, in that order. For example, "pull carbon slips" has allowances of personal = 5%, fatigue = 4%, and delay = 2%.

Appendix - Job Descriptions

A. Job Title - discharger

The discharger will be directly under the assistant supervisor and shall be responsible for collecting the books out of the drop boxes, removing the carbon charge slip from the back of the books, placing the "no carbon" books on a list, stamping the carbon charge slips with the time and date returned, and sorting the books by floor sections.

Procedure:

1. At designated times during the day the discharger takes the flat-bed truck and, following the prescribed path, picks up books from the drop boxes.

2. Upon returning from picking up the bags from drop boxes the discharger will:

   a. pick up book from bag

   b. open up the back of the book and remove the "carbon" charge slip

   c. place the charge slip in a box

3. Upon completing the discharging operation, the discharger will stamp the carbon charge slip with time and date.

4. The discharger will place group of carbons in a place to be taken to the Circulation Department.

5. The discharger will move books to sorting area and sort by floor section.

B. Job Title - loader

The loader will be directly under the assistant supervisor and shall be responsible for sorting the books onto trucks by call number, checking a loaded truck for hold books, removing any hold books found and placing them in the designated area for hold books.

Procedure:

1. At scheduled times during the day the loader will move empty trucks (if needed) to the shelves he is assigned to work on.

2. He will sort books onto trucks by call number.

3. He will move the second row of books into front position

after the front row has been exhausted.

4. Upon completing the loading of a truck, he will move the truck to the check area.

5. He will check the truck for hold books by comparing hold slips to books on the truck.

6. He will remove any hold books, place the hold slip in the book and place the book in a designated area.

7. He will move the truck to the storage area to await distribution of the books to their floors.

C. Job Title - shelver

A shelver is directly under an assistant supervisor and is responsible for shelving returned books, picking up the ranges, changing light bulbs, and transporting books on the temporary shelves to the stackroom. (Books on the temporary shelves belong on other floors.)

Procedure:

1. The shelver will pick up a light bulb and place it in the pocket of his library coat or on the truck from which books are being shelved.

2. He will move the loaded truck to the area the books are to be shelved in.

3. He will shelve books.

4. When books are found on the ranges during shelving, the books are:

   a. Shelved if book belongs in the immediate area (normally immediate means the same range)

   b. Placed on truck if the book does not belong in the immediate area

5. When a burned out light bulb is encountered, it is replaced with the one carried. (If more than one burned out bulb is found, return to the temporary shelves and pick up a bulb to replace the burned out bulb.)

6. Upon returning to the stacks department, a load of books from the temporary shelves and belonging on other floors will be returned to the stacks department. A truck will

88

be used if one is empty; if not, the books will be person-
ally carried.

Rule:

Any person returning to the stacks department from the stacks
will bring books from the temporary shelves with him.

D. Trading-Trucks Procedure

1. Pick up all hold books which have been processed since the
   last trip to the Circulation Department and place on the
   truck.
2. Take carbons that have been processed.
3. Transport books and carbons to Circulation Department.
4. Unload the hold books.
5. Pick up books returned to Circulation Department.
6. Pick up hold slips.
7. Transport books and hold slips to stack department.
8. File the hold slips by floor and call number.

Feasibility Study of a Single Point Exterior Book Return System

By: M. C. Drott, L. L. Hoag

Objective

The objective of this project was to evaluate various methods of exterior book return. The cost of such systems was the primary point for evaluation. This cost must be justified by the expected usage of each system.

Background

Exterior chutes for facilitating the return of books have been used successfully in libraries. For example, book-return chutes are incorporated into the building design at the University of Michigan Undergraduate Library. A chute enables book return at any time, and also provides for the protection of returned volumes against theft or adverse weather conditions.

Present System:

All returned books are processed for reshelving by the Stacks Section located in the basement of the library. The receiving points for books returned from outside circulation are four exterior drop boxes located near the entrances on the north and west sides of the building (see diagram). An additional receiving point is the circulation desk located just inside the front door on the first floor. Drop-box collections are made by hand carrying books in canvas "shopping" bags from the drop box to the stacks section. Books returned to the circulation desk are placed on a book cart. Stacks Section workers "trade" carts, leaving an empty cart while moving the loaded cart to the basement via the building elevator.

The cost of the present system is calculated as follows:

Present Collection System Cost

1. Walking time per year

distance walked per collection (3 trips) = 3,129 feet.

$$\frac{3{,}129 \text{ ft./coll.}}{208.4 \text{ ft.}} \times 1 \text{ min.} \times \frac{12 \text{ coll./day} \times 340 \text{ days/yr}}{60 \text{ min./hr.}} = 1{,}020 \text{ hrs. per year}$$

Possible Chute Locations

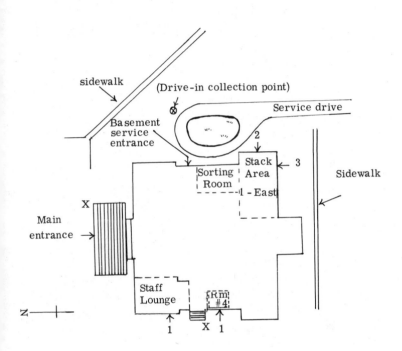

Key:

→ Indicates a possible chute location
X Indicates present drop boxes
⊗ Drive-in collection point

2. Book unloading time per year

    8 min./coll. x 12 coll./day x 340 days/year   60 min./hr. =
    544 hrs./yr.

3. Trading-truck time per year (Interior pick-up)

    a. Elevator time = 126.84 sec. (wait) + 32.06 sec. (ride) =
       158.90 sec.

    b. Walking time = $2 \times \left[\dfrac{279 \text{ ft.} \times 60 \text{ sec.}}{208 \text{ ft.}} \right] = 160.96$ sec.

              Total time/trip = 319.9 sec.

    319.9 sec./coll. x 6 coll./day x 1 hr./3,600 sec. x 340 day/yr.
            = 181.3 hrs./yr.

4. Total time of present method = 1,746.3 hours per year. *

5. Total cost of present method:

    1,746.3 hours/yr. x $1.19/hr. = $2,078 per year.

The primary disadvantage to the library is the large annual man-hour requirement. It is estimated that Stacks Section personnel walk 2,420 miles per year to collect books.

The above method was analyzed in the "Reshelving of Books" project, and a proposal was developed in which each drop box would be equipped with a canvas-bag insert. These bags, which would be filled as books were deposited, would be removed from the boxes and transported via a flat-bed cart to the Stacks Section sorting area. At the time of each collection, full bags in the drop boxes would be replaced by empty ones. This procedure results in a savings on the box unloading time and reduces the number of trips per collection by two-thirds. The specific advantages to this proposal would be (1) a significant annual savings ($1,014) over the present system, and (2) a minimal cost ($175) to change over from the present system.

Analysis:

To select the proper location and the most desirable method for the collection of books, it is necessary to evaluate the factors of cost, customer service, and the effect of a particular alternative on other library functions. Five types of book-return systems were considered in this study: (1) an exterior chute emptying into an

---

* This differs from the figure presented in Analysis of Book Reshelving because of the inclusion of 181.3 hours for interior pick-up in this calculation.

interior truck, (2) an exterior chute connected to a gravity roller conveyor which returns books directly to the Stacks Section, (3) an exterior chute connected to a combination belt-roller conveyor, (4) an exterior chute connected to a powered belt conveyor, and (5) the grouping of all drop boxes at a single exterior location.

Before a specific collection process is established, the receiving location for returned books must be determined. The alternatives are single-point or multi-point collection. A multi-point system, such as the present drop-box procedure, offers customer service in the form of a variety of locations for book return. However, in this type of system a high cost of providing this service is experienced, since Stacks Section personnel must travel a relatively long distance to collect books. A single point of collection, on the other hand, enables easier and much less costly book collection by Stacks Section personnel. The main issue in selecting a single location is whether or not such a collection point will be utilized by a significant number of library customers. The potential savings to be realized is definitely related to this utilization. The locations considered were (1) the west side of the library near the west entrance, (2) the east side of the library, (3) the south side of the library, and (4) the "drive in" collection point near the east side of the library.

In order to evaluate these various proposals it is necessary to estimate the collection times involved. To do this, sample times were taken for various activities and the appropriate transportation distances were measured. The calculations are as follows:

1) West side chute collection time
   a) Time to switch trucks = 15 sec.
   b) Transport time $[213 \text{ ft. } \times \frac{60 \text{ sec.}}{208 \text{ ft.}}] + [213 \text{ ft. } \times \frac{60 \text{ sec.}}{158 \text{ ft.}}] = 142.3$ sec.
   $$\text{total time/trip} \qquad = 157.3 \text{ sec.}$$

2) East side chute collection time
   a) Time to switch trucks = 15 sec.
   b) Transport time $2 \times [57 \text{ ft. } \times \frac{60 \text{ sec.}}{208 \text{ ft.}}] + [57 \text{ ft. } \times \frac{60 \text{ sec.}}{158 \text{ ft.}}] = 54.53$ sec.
   $$\text{total time/trip} \qquad = 69.53 \text{ sec.}$$

3) South side chute collection time
   a) Time to switch trucks = 15 sec.

Analysis of a University Library

b) Transport time $\left[84 \text{ ft. } x \dfrac{60 \text{ sec.}}{208 \text{ ft.}}\right] + \left[84 \text{ ft. } x \dfrac{60 \text{ sec.}}{158 \text{ ft.}}\right]$ = 56. 13 sec.

total time/trip = 71. 13 sec.

4) Drive-in collection time

a) Transport time 390 ft. x $\dfrac{60 \text{ sec.}}{208. 4 \text{ ft.}}$ =112. 28 sec.

b) Unloading time 4 min./coll. x 60 sec./min. =240. sec.

total time-trip =352. 28 sec.

As one would expect, the three methods which do not require workers to leave the building are the fastest. Among these the only differences are attributable to differences in distance from the collection point to the stack room.

The use of a chute is limited by friction to short distances.
It is possible to use other types of conveyors to bring the books directly to the work area, thus eliminating walking time. There are
three important types of conveyors that might be applicable: gravity-
roller or wheel conveyors, which need a slight downward incline to
operate; roller-belt conveyors, which are motor driven and can operate on the level or slight inclines; and powered-belt conveyors,
which are also motor driven and can handle heavy loads at steep
inclines. These conveyors are listed in increasing order of initial
cost. Any conveyor system would require a chute entrance into the
library.

In order to estimate conveyor costs, sketches were prepared
for each chute location. Costs were calculated using data supplied
by several conveyor manufacturers. A sample sketch and cost calculation are shown in figure 1. The costs of the other systems are
presented in the table below.

If the library were to purchase one of these systems, it would
be using money that could be put to use elsewhere in the library. To
recognize this lost opportunity we introduce the idea of a capital recovery cost:

Captial Recovery Factor = $\dfrac{i(1 + i)^n}{(1 + i)^{n}-1}$

Where i represents the opportunity cost (this might be an interest
cost in the case of borrowed money). The time over which the money
is to be recovered is represented by n. In this case i = 4% and n =
5 years.

94

An Exterior Book Return System

Cost of Conveyor (estimated) -
East Side Path 1

I. Deposit Point (Made of Steel)
   Enclosure $300
   Chute   100 $400

II. Roller Conveyor
    Straight Sections $444
    (37 ft. x $12/ft.)
    Curved Section   300
    (2)
    Supports (5 x $8)   40 $784

III. Skid Section
     Chute $100
     Support   8 $108

Total (not including installation)
= $1,292

Proposed East Side Book Returns

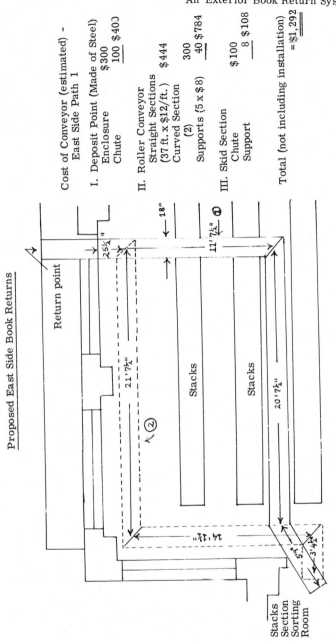

Analysis of a University Library

Capital Recovery Factor = . 225
Annual Cost to be Recovered = (. 225) x Cost of System

This calculation more accurately represents the true cost to the library, since it recognizes the fact that the library has only limited resources.

We must still determine the cost when part of the books are returned to an exterior point and the rest to the loan desk. For example, to calculate the annual costs for 50% and 100% exterior return we must first calculate the time for interior returns.

Based on an annual circulation of 200, 000 books, the truck-trading time if 50% (100, 000 books) are returned to the main desk:

(1) trips presently made for 60, 000 books = $6 \frac{\text{trips}}{\text{day}}$

trips required for 50% = $6 \times \frac{100,000}{60,000} = 10 \frac{\text{trips}}{\text{day}}$

(2) $\frac{\text{time}}{\text{year}} = 345. 4 \frac{\text{sec.}}{\text{trip}} \times 10 \frac{\text{trips}}{\text{day}} \times 340 \frac{\text{days}}{\text{year}} \times \frac{1 \text{ hr.}}{3,600 \text{ sec.}} = 326 \frac{\text{hours}}{\text{year}}$

Using this in combination with the costs calculated before:

A) West chute

(1) if 50% are returned to the exterior collection point - collection
time = $157. 4 \frac{\text{sec.}}{\text{trip}} \times 10 \frac{\text{trips}}{\text{day}} \times 340 \frac{\text{days}}{\text{year}} \times \frac{1 \text{ hr.}}{3,600 \text{ sec.}} = 148. 7 \frac{\text{hours}}{\text{year}}$

trade-truck time = $\underline{ 326.}$

total time/year = $474. 7 \frac{\text{hours}}{\text{year}}$

(2) if 100% are returned to the exterior collection point - collection
time = $157. 4 \frac{\text{sec.}}{\text{trip}} \times 20 \frac{\text{trips}}{\text{day}} \times 340 \frac{\text{days}}{\text{year}} \times \frac{1 \text{ hr.}}{3,600 \text{ sec.}} = 297. 3 \frac{\text{hours}}{\text{year}}$

B) East chute

(1) if 50% are returned to the exterior collection point - collection
time = $53. 06 \frac{\text{sec.}}{\text{trip}} \times 10 \frac{\text{trips}}{\text{day}} \times 340 \frac{\text{days}}{\text{year}} \times \frac{1 \text{ hr.}}{3,600 \text{ sec.}} = 50. 1 \frac{\text{hours}}{\text{year}}$

trade-truck time = $\underline{ 326. 00}$

total time/year = 376. 11 hrs.

(2) if 100% are returned to the exterior collection point - collection
time = $53. 06 \frac{\text{sec.}}{\text{trip}} \times 20 \frac{\text{trips}}{\text{day}} \times 340 \frac{\text{days}}{\text{year}} \times \frac{1 \text{ hr.}}{3,600 \text{ sec.}} = 100. 2 \frac{\text{hours}}{\text{year}}$

C) South chute

(1) if 50% are returned to the exterior collection point - collection

$$\text{time} = 71.09 \frac{\text{sec.}}{\text{trip}} \times 10 \frac{\text{trips}}{\text{day}} \times 340 \frac{\text{days}}{\text{year}} \times \frac{1 \text{ hr.}}{3,600 \text{ sec.}} = 67.1 \frac{\text{hours}}{\text{year}}$$

$$\text{trade truck time} \quad = 326.$$

$$\text{total time/year} \quad = 393.1 \frac{\text{hours}}{\text{year}}$$

(2) if 100% are returned to the exterior collection point - collection

$$\text{time} = 71.09 \frac{\text{sec.}}{\text{trip}} \times 20 \frac{\text{trips}}{\text{day}} \times 340 \frac{\text{days}}{\text{year}} \times \frac{1 \text{ hr.}}{3,600 \text{ sec.}} = 134.3 \frac{\text{hours}}{\text{year}}$$

For the present case, we know that 30% of the books are returned to the main desk and 70% are returned to the drop boxes. Since the drive-in collection box proposal is so similar to the present system, the same percentages will be applied to both systems.

D) Canvas bags (70% drop box, 30% main desk)

(1) Present (canvas bag) - walking time/yr. $= 1,206 \frac{\text{ft.}}{\text{coll.}} \times \frac{1 \text{ min.}}{208.4 \text{ ft.}} \times$

$$12 \frac{\text{coll.}}{\text{day}} \times 340 \frac{\text{days}}{\text{year}} \times \frac{1 \text{ hr.}}{3,600 \text{ sec.}} = 393.5 \frac{\text{hours}}{\text{year}}$$

$$\text{box unloading time} = 4 \frac{\text{min.}}{\text{coll.}} \times \frac{12 \times 340}{60} = 272 \frac{\text{hours}}{\text{year}}$$

$$\text{trade truck/time} = 32.6 \times 6 \frac{\text{coll.}}{\text{day}} = 195.6 \frac{\text{hours}}{\text{year}}$$

$$\text{total time/yr.} \quad 861.1 \frac{\text{hours}}{\text{year}}$$

(2) Drive-in (canvas bag) - collection time $= 39 \frac{\text{ft.}}{\text{coll.}} \times 12$

$$\frac{\text{coll.}}{\text{day}} \times 340 \frac{\text{days}}{\text{year}} \times 208.4 \frac{\text{ft.}}{\text{min.}} \times \frac{1 \text{ hr.}}{3,600 \text{ sec.}} = 127 \frac{\text{hrs.}}{\text{year}}$$

$$\text{unloading time} \quad = 272 \frac{\text{hrs.}}{\text{year}}$$

$$\text{trade truck time} \quad = 195.6 \frac{\text{hours}}{\text{year}}$$

$$\text{total time/yr.} \quad 480.3$$

All of the relevant costs are tabulated in the table below. The sidewalk cost would result from a short extension of the existing pavement to the chute. Installation costs are those for the return chute only. The variety of conveyor proposals and the fact that conveyor installation would be relatively cheap made it infeasible to figure costs for each conveyor type separately. The largest single installation cost for a conveyor system is the cost of knocking out a part of the wall, and this cost is already included in the chute installation cost. Labor costs were based on $1.19 per hour, the average effective hourly cost of the workers involved.

97

ALTERNATE SYSTEM COSTS FOR RETURNING BOOKS

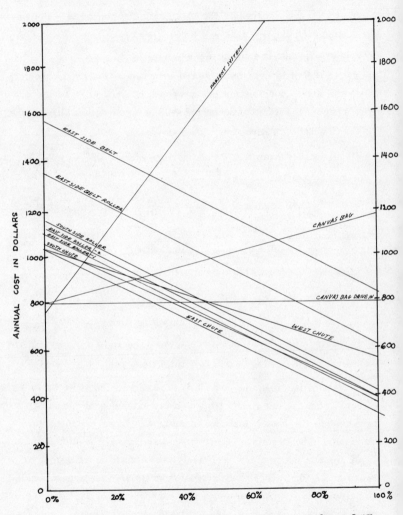

PERCENTAGE OF CIRCULATION RETURNING TO EXTERIOR COLLECTION POINT

We can see that these costs and savings are heavily dependent on the percent of books which are returned to the outside depository. To see this clearly we refer to the figure entitled "Alternate System Costs for Returning Books." The cost for various percentages of exterior return are plotted and form a straight line. Using this chart we can calculate the annual cost of each of the systems for any return pattern. For example to find the cost of the canvas bag system when 80% of the books are returned to the exterior point; first locate 80% on the horizontal (exterior return) scale. Follow this line up until it meets the line labeled "canvas bags". Now look directly across at the annual cost scale. The cost of this system with 80% exterior returns is about $1,100.

Some additional considerations are also relevant. The west side location does not appear to be desirable for two reasons. First, it is in an area which is utilized by Bindery Preparation and an employee lounge. Second, book deposit at the west side would require substantial travel to and from the Stacks Section making this location quite expensive. The east and south locations are adjacent to the Stacks Section, facilitating low labor costs per collection. It is believed that the east location is closer to heavy pedestrian traffic than is the south collection point. Either of these locations would require the construction of a short section of sidewalk, but the cost would be relatively small. The drive-in collection point (also on the east side but away from the building) would be an especially convenient location, since it is adjacent to the sidewalk and also to the driveway. It is concluded, therefore, that a single location on the east side of the library (either adjacent to or near the building) would be the most efficient location if customer patronage could be assured.

A roller conveyor represents the most economical system of book collection, but it has one major drawback. Any conveyor system leading into the Stacks Section would limit the use of a portion of existing stacks to inactive storage, because the conveyor would become a permanent obstruction to truck and cart movement in that area. Thus, in view of this consideration, the east chute seems most feasible.

Analysis of a University Library

Annual Savings Comparison

Proposal	Annual Cost ($) carts	chute entrance	conveyor	canvas bags	sidewalk	installation costs	annual recovery costs***	100% exterior return labor	100% exterior return total**	50% exterior return labor	50% exterior return total**	Annual Savings 100%	Annual Savings 50%
East Roller path 1	-	400	892	-	60	150	338	-	338	388	726	1740	1352
path 2	-	400	1006	-	60	150	363	-	363	388	751	1715	1327
East Chute	150	400	116	-	60	150	197	120	317	448	645	1761	1433
West Chute	150	400	116	-	70	150	199	353	552	565	764	1526	1314
South Roller	-	400	1064	-	139	150	395	-	395	388	783	1683	1295
South Chute	150	400	116	-	139	150	215	160	375	468	683	1703	1395
East Belt	-	400	3000	-	60	150	812	-	812	388	1200	1266	878
East Belt Roller	-	400	2010	-	60	150	590	-	590	388	978	1488	1100
Canvas Bag Present	75	-	-	100	-	-	39	*1025	*1064	*1025	*1064	*1014	*1014
Canvas Bag Drive-in	75	-	-	100	-	-	39	*572	*611	*572	*611	*1467	*1467
Present	-	-	-	-	-	-	-	*2078	*2078	*2078	*2078	-	-

* The percentage return for the Present, Canvas Bag Present, and Canvas Bag Drive-in proposals are 70% for drop boxes, and 30% for return to the main desk, which was estimated by actual survey.

** Total annual cost equals labor cost plus conversion recovery cost.

*** Based on total recovery in five years at 4% interest.

100

Conclusions

The following considerations are believed to be the governing factors in the selection of a book return system:

(1) the annual cost

(2) the costs of conversion

(3) customer acceptance and utilization

(4) the effect on other library functions

After thoroughly evaluating all the possible collection systems, the following two proposals were selected as the most feasible alternatives.

Alternative One:

In the short run it is recommended that all exterior drop boxes be concentrated at a single location on the east side of the General Library. Each drop box would be equipped with a self-loading canvas bag. Collections would be made manually, with the aid of a flat-bed cart to enable complete drop-box collection in a single trip. This short-run proposal is selected as the immediate recommendation because:

(1) the cost per year of drop-box collections will be reduced from $2,100 to approximately $611. The latter figure includes a conversion cost of $175 which is amortized at 4% over a five-year period.

(2) the present drop-box utilization is known to account for approximately 70% of the total book collection from outside circulation. The remaining 30% are returned to the main desk in the Circulation Department.

(3) this single location for all drop boxes will be near that of the proposed long-range chute location (discussed below). Potential customer acceptance of a chute, therefore, can be measured by the aggregate response to grouping drop boxes at a single location.

Alternative Two:

In the long run the most economical system for book return is believed to be an exterior chute which would enter the east side of the General Library near the southeast corner of the building. There are two reasons for recommending a delay in the adoption of this proposal:

101

Analysis of a University Library

(1) The transition costs for a chute are approximately $876, and the profitability of such an expenditure will, in part, be dependent upon customer response, a factor which can be better assessed after the implementation of the short-range recommendations.

(2) An addition is presently being considered for the area south of the library. New traffic patterns may make some location in this structure a more desirable return point.

It should be noted that a fully used chute return would have the following advantages:

(1) A savings of $1,761 per year would be realized over the present system, or an annual cost requirement of $317 for book collection (which includes the amortized conversion costs), compared with the $2,078 cost of the present system.

(2) All books would be returned inside the building, and would, therefore, not be subjected to weather elements or possible theft.

(3) The critical scheduling of personnel to collect books during periods of abnormally high book-return or adverse weather would be eliminated.

Investigation of a Centralized Book Relabeling System
for the Divisional Libraries

By: R. E. Beck

Objective

Cataloging and purchasing are centralized for the divisional
libraries at the University of Michigan. The question asked by the
library administration is, "Is it more economical and practical to
centralize the relabeling of books?"

Background

Currently, each divisional library is responsible for its own
relabeling and consequently has developed its own procedure for relabeling. These procedures differ from each other mainly in the
choice of materials used in relabeling and the time it takes to re-
label.

There are two types of paper labels, each with the name of
the divisional library printed on it, --the Randall label and the Avery
label. The Avery label has a pressure-sensitive adhesive, while the
Randall label has a lick-type adhesive. The Avery label can be attached by simply removing its protective backing and pressing it to
the book. The Randall label can be licked, or a dab of Magic-Mend
glue can be smeared on the back of the label and the label then applied to the book. The call number is lettered on the label by hand
with pen and India ink either before or after the label is attached to
the book. In some divisionals, Plasti-lac Book Spray is sprayed on
the labels after they have been lettered and attached.

If one takes advantage of quantity discounts, it is possible to
purchase an eight-ounce bottle of Magic-Mend glue for $1.30. Rough
estimates indicate that 1,200 labels can be glued per bottle. Thus,
the cost per label for glue is $.0011. Similarly, one 16 ounce can
of Plasti-Lac Bookspray that costs $1.80 can spray an estimated 500
labels. Thus, the cost per label for spray is $.0036. The costs of
the present relabeling methods are found in Table A. The times listed
in the last row are average times taken after the workplace had been

103

Analysis of a University Library

set up and all the materials had been gathered. The Catalog Department, in which the books are initially labeled, uses the Avery label and attaches it by placing a Teflon shield over the label and running a heating iron over it. This method gives the strongest and longest-adhering label. The Catalog Department is in an advantageous position. Because of the fact that they do a large amount of labeling per day, they can have a heating iron and a person who is skilled at lettering. This combination produces quality labeling. The divisional libraries cannot have heating irons because of the fire hazard, and they do not do enough relabeling to require a "skilled letterer." This is not to say that the divisional library cannot have a person who can produce neat, legible lettering.

Analysis

    Because each divisional librarian involved had little or no

Table A - Cost of Various Relabeling Methods	Method 1	Method 2	Method 3	Method 4	Method 5	Method 6
Avery Label	$.0030	$.0030				
Randall Label			$.0030	$.0030	$.0030	$.0030
Book Spray	$.0036				$.0036	$.0036
Glue				$.0011		$.0011
Labor	$.0728	$.0625	$.0728	$.0833	$.0833	$.0938
Total Cost Per Label	$.0794	$.0655	$.0758	$.0774	$.0899	$.1015
Time Per Label (Min.)	3.5	3.0	3.5	4.0	4.0	4.5

104

Table B - Annual Cost of Relabeling

Divisional Library	(1) Number of Days in Sample	(2) Number of Books Re-labeled	(3) Books Re-labeled Per Day (2)/(1)	(4) Books Re-labeled Per Year (3) x 350 days/year	(5) Relabeling Cost Per Book	(6) Annual Cost (4) x (5)
Education	51	25	.490	172	$.0794	$ 13.66
Architecture	30	21	.700	245	$.1015	$ 24.87
Engin. - Trans.	14	150	10.714	3,750	$.0899	$ 37.13
Mathematics	43	198	4.605	1,612	$.1015	$163.62
Social Work	51	10	.196	69	$.0794	$ 5.48
Library Science	51	2	.039	14	$.0758	$ 1.06
Museums	24	26	1.083	379	$.0655	$ 24.82
Physics - Astro.	39	115	2.949	1,032	$.0874	$ 90.20
Chem. - Pharm.	44	20	.455	159	$.0655	$ 10.41
Fine Arts	24	66	2.750	963	$.0655	$ 63.08
Total						$734.33

105

idea of the amount of relabeling done in any period of time, they
were asked to keep a list of the call numbers of the books relabeled
during a period of approximately a month. This would give some
indication as to the amount and quality of the relabeling done in the
divisional libraries. The results are summarized in Table B, along
with the calculation of the annual cost. There are 350 days that the
libraries are open, taking into account holidays and slack days.

The quality of the relabeling was measured by going to each
divisional library with the lists of call numbers and, after finding
the book, checking the label for legibility and quality of adherence
to the book. The results of this study indicate that the quality of
relabeling done in the divisional libraries is comparable to the
labeling done in the Catalog Department.

As a result of talks with section heads of the Catalog Department, it was concluded that centralizing the book relabeling process
would be infeasible. It was found that the Catalog Department would
need to hire a full-time person in order to handle the relabeling
chore. But this would be impractical, because the relabeling would
only amount to about 1/3 of his time. Also, more space would be
required, and this space is not readily available. Centralizing relabeling would mean that a book would be out of circulation for at
least one day. This means the divisional librarian would have no
control over the book and could not lend the book to a student who
might request it. Under the present system she could locate it and
lend it out in a matter of minutes. Further, any time savings to a
divisional library would be so small that they could not convert it
to cash by reducing their personnel budget. Finally, the total annual
cost of $734 indicates that any cash savings to the over-all system
would be small. However, there could be some improvement in the
quality of relabeling. For instance, by having one person responsible
for relabeling, that person could acquire a lettering skill through
his continued relabeling. Also, it is recommended that the divisionals let the books to be relabeled accumulate for a period of time
so that the cost per label of setting up the materials for relabeling
is lowered.

As is usually the case in a preliminary study, new problems were discovered. It was found in our study that some percentage of the Avery labels applied without using a heating iron do not adhere very well in the early life of the label. The edges of these labels curl and peel loose, and the labels eventually fall off. The question was raised, "Which label should the divisional libraries use?" The Avery label is less costly but has a questionable early life. On the other hand, the Randall label adheres well but is more costly.

The criterion involved is one of the least cost per year. This principle is used by librarians when deciding which of two different types of equipment to purchase. Say the market offers two different types of electric typewriters. Typewriter A costs $500 and is reported by the manufacturer to have a useful life of five years. Typewriter B costs $750 and is reported to have a useful life of ten years. Applying the above criterion, the annual cost of typewriter A is $100 ($500/5 years) while that of typewriter B is $75 ($750/10 years). The choice, then, would be to purchase typewriter B because of the lower annual cost.

However, it was found that it was impossible to determine how long the labels last. So, because of the lack of data to the contrary, it has been assumed that if an Avery label adheres well after the first year, it will have the same life as a Randall label.

A procedure using Magic-Mend Glue and Plasti-lac Book Spray to apply the Randall label was considered as the best alternative to compare with the Avery label. This procedure gave the Randall label its longest life and agreed with our assumption about the lives of the two labels. The cost per label for a Randall label using this procedure is $.1015 and that for an Avery label applied without using a heating iron or book spray is $.0655. Call the average life of the Randall labels, R, and the average life of the Avery labels, A. The annual cost of the Randall label then becomes $.1015/R and the annual cost of the Avery label is $.0655/A years. One of the conditions in which we are interested is the one where the annual costs of both labels are the same. Expressed mathematically it becomes,

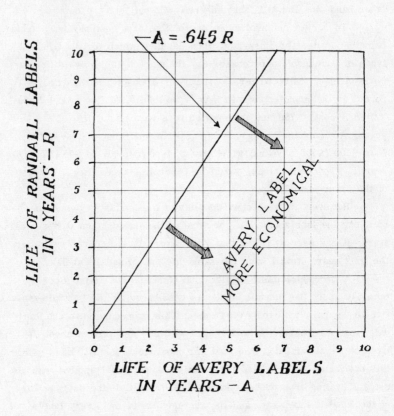

FIGURE 1 - GRAPH OF EQUATION (1)

$$\frac{\$.0655}{A} = \frac{\$.1015}{R}$$

Rearranging the terms and solving for A as an unknown we obtain equation (1),

(1) $A = .645 \ R$

This equation was plotted on a "R" versus "A" graph in Figure 1. If the point corresponding to the actual average lives of the Randall and Avery labels is above and to the left of this straight line then the Randall label is more economical. If the point is to the right and below the graph, then the Avery is more economical. However, we stated earlier that we assumed that if an Avery label sticks for one year its life is as long as the Randall label. Say some number, X, of 100 Avery labels do not stick for more than one year and the rest, (100-X) labels have a life of R years, the average life of a Randall label. Then the average life of 100 Avery labels, A, is expressed mathematically,

(2) $A = \dfrac{X(1 \text{ year}) + (100\text{-}X) \ (R \text{ years})}{100}$

This will be referred to as equation (2). As an example, assume 40 Avery labels out of 100 have fallen off at the end of one year. Then $X = 40$ in our equation and the average life of an Avery label then becomes,

(3) $A = \dfrac{(40) \ (1) + (100\text{-}40) \ (R)}{100} = .4 + .6R$

This was plotted on the graph as shown in Figure 2. This straight line intersects with the graph of equation (1) at a point R 8.89 years and A 5.73 years. This intersection means that if 40% of the Avery labels do not last more than one year, the Randall labels will have to have an average life of 8.89 years in order that the costs per year of both labels be the same. A more useful variable is the percentage of Avery labels that do not last more than one year. Call this percentage P. Equation (2) then becomes,

(3) $A = \dfrac{P + (100\text{-}P)R}{100}$

By picking different percentages, P, and plotting them, we get some interesting results. For example, equation (3) was also plotted taking the percentage to be 30%, as shown in figure 3. This straight line did not intersect the graph of equation (1). This means

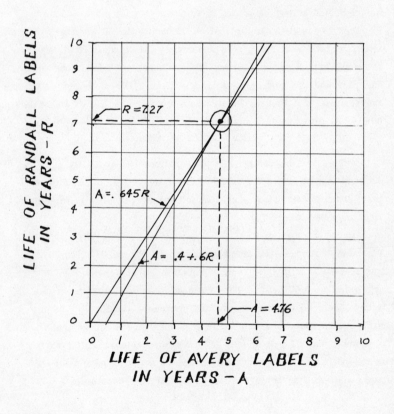

FIGURE 2 - GRAPH OF
EQUATIONS
(1) AND (2)

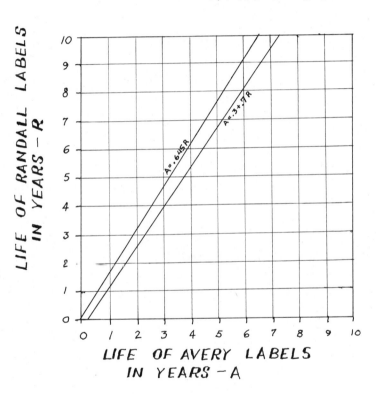

FIGURE 3- GRAPH OF
EQUATIONS
(1) AND (3)
WITH P=30%

that regardless of the lives of the two labels the Avery label is more economical, because all possible lives of the labels for P= 30% lie in the region where the Avery label is more economical.

By varying or choosing different P's, the slope or "tilt" of the graph of equation (3) changes. The question we now ask is, "At what maximum percentage is the Avery label always more economical?", or what mathematically is the same, "At what percentage are the graphs of equations (1) and (3) parallel?"

For two straight lines to be parallel, the coefficients of the "R's" in equations (1) and (3) must be equal. From equation (1) the coefficient of R is .645 and from equation (3) the coefficient is $\frac{100-P}{100}$. Equating them we obtain,

$$.645 = \frac{100-P}{100}$$

Solving for P, we get P= 35.5%.

The main point of the whole analysis is this: if the percentage of Avery labels that do not last more than one year is greater than 35.5%, we would have to know the average life of either the Avery or Randall label in order to determine which is more economical. But if the percentage is less than 35.5%, the Avery labels will always be the most economical.

Conclusion

From our survey of relabeled books, we discovered that 18 out of 220 labels had started to peel loose and probably would not last more than one year. This percentage is 8.2%, far below the critical 35.5%. In our talks with the librarians, no indication was given that one-third of the relabeled books needed relabeling at the end of a year. Therefore, it was concluded that the Avery labels were the most practical and economical labels to be used for re-labeling in the divisional libraries. Book spray should not be used because it causes the labels to curl.

Summary

Three findings emerged from this study:

(1) The function of relabeling books housed in divisional libraries should continue to be performed by the divisional libraries.

(2) The quality of relabeling done by the divisional libraries

is comparable to that done in the Catalog Department.

(3) The Avery label is more economical than the Randall label and should be used by the divisional libraries.

Methods Analysis of Exit Control and Charge-Out Functions

By: M. C. Drott, G. C. Ehrnstrum, L. L. Hoag

Objectives:

The concern of this study is the reduction of patron waiting time at the library exit. The control the library has over its books must be maintained at its present level.

Background:

The exit control clerk serves two functions: (1) preventing the unauthorized removal of volumes from the library building, and (2) charging out library volumes. All books, briefcases, large bags, and large purses are checked as the library users leave the building. The charge procedure is:

1. Library user fills out a pre-dated charge slip and presents it with the book to the exit control worker.

2. The library user's University I. D. is checked.

3. The call number on the charge slip is checked against the call number on the book, and corrected if necessary.

4. The exit control worker checks the due date of the book and changes the pre-dated charge slip if necessary.

5. The worker initials the charge slips.

6. The worker punches the charge slips.

7. The worker separates the charge slips,

8. The worker places original charge slip in desk file, and

9. The worker places carbon charge slip in the back of the book.

During slack periods, Circulation Department personnel on exit control duty perform miscellaneous tasks such as tabbing charges, sorting charges by shelf list order, etc.

The exit control operation has an annual cost of approximately $9,000. The operation requires that at least one person be on exit control duty during all the hours the library is open. When a large number of people are exiting, two to four library workers are on exit control duty. Even with all the exit control desks open, long lines form several times during the day. This has caused many user

114

complaints.

Analysis:

In order to define the present situation and to evaluate proposed systems, the data summarized below were collected.

Tabulation of Results from Exit Survey

Distribution of people exiting from library:

People exiting empty handed	52. 4%
People exiting with material that must be checked	37. 1%
People exiting who charge books	10. 5%

Distribution of people charging books:

Number of books charged	% of people in this classification
1	28. 85
2	23. 30
3	13. 95
4	11. 10
5	6. 55
more than 5	16. 25

Average times to complete exit activities:

Exiting empty handed	2 seconds
Exiting with material that must be checked	6 seconds
Exiting and charging	16. 15 charging
	6. 00 exiting
	22. 15 seconds

Distribution of charging times (including exiting):

Average charging time for 1 and 2 books	20. 6 seconds
Average charging time for 3 or more books	65. 6 seconds

In working with these figures, "percentage of occurance" can be
combined with "time" to produce averages. Thus the overall average
exiting time per customer would be computed as follows:

Suppose 100 people leave the library. From the percentages in
the table we can say that 52 of them will be without books, 37 will
have materials to be checked, and 11 people will charge books. Now
using the times we can calculate the total time that it will take for
all 100 people to leave.

$$
\begin{array}{rcl}
52 \text{ people X 2 seconds each} & = 104 & \text{seconds} \\
37 \text{ people X 6 seconds each} & = 222 & \text{seconds} \\
11 \text{ people X 22. 15 sec. ea.} & = 243. 65 & \text{seconds} \\
\hline
& 569. 65 & \text{seconds}
\end{array}
$$

So 100 people will take a total of 569. 65 seconds to exit. Dividing the total time by the number of people, the average time per person is 5. 7 seconds. This technique of compiling a weighted average is used throughout this report.

Proposed Systems:

Three approaches were used in an attempt to improve the exiting procedure. These approaches were: 1) modification of present procedure, 2) adoption of an entirely new procedure, and 3) controlled exiting, involves the specialization of exiting lines; i. e. , people with no books to charge, people with one book to charge, people with two books to charge, and people with more than two books to charge would exit in different lines. An analysis was made using the weighted average technique shown above. Average waiting times in separated lines were compared with those for the same number of undisciplined queues. The system was shown to be unstable. Under the proper set of conditions, extemely long lines would form. This would cause the exiting discipline to deteriorate, and destroy all usefulness of the specialized lines. To determine whether an entirely new procedure should be adopted, the present circulation system was compared with the systems included in Study of Circulation Control Systems. [1] After these comparisons, it was found that all the systems, except the marginal punched charge card system, were more costly than the present system.

The marginal punched charge card system has a potential savings over the present system of approximately $200 annually. This savings, although it would pay for the necessary equipment in a year, does not justify adoption of the system. A switch from the present system would require more man hours in training personnel and in adjusting to the new system than could be recovered in the relatively short period the new system would be used.

The administrative personnel of the General Library are planning to adopt an IBM circulation system within a few years. Thus, a conversion to a new circulation system, which is not an

IBM system, would have only a few years to pay for itself. In the short span of a few years the library staff, faculty, and students would have to adjust to two different charging procedures. This would probably cause much confusion and many complaints.

The last approach to the problem, alteration of the present charging and exit control operation, involved placing as much work as possible on the library users and simplifying the present procedure. If the student ID cards were used to stamp the name of the borrower on the charge slip, checking of ID's and punching of charge slips could be eliminated. Since the ID cards do not have the students' addresses on them, the overdue process would be complicated. The additional time required to process the overdues would be greater than the savings at exit control. The use of plastic borrowers' cards with the library user's name and address would be prohibitively expensive.

The library throws away $290 worth of pre-dated charge slips annually. This cost can be eliminated and the exiting time can be slightly reduced by eliminating pre-dating, eliminating punching of charge slips, and adopting dating of charge slips at the exit control desks.

The punching operation was designed to verify that a book had been charged. If this operation and the pre-dating operation were eliminated, dating of the charge slips at the charging desks would provide a method of verifying that a book has been charged, and it would provide the due date of the book. Two additional daters of the type being used presently would have to be purchased at a cost of approximately $50 apiece. Thus the above changes would have an initial cost of $100. The time saved by the above change is small compared to the total time spent on exit control.

Savings for Dating at Exit

Machine dating time:
210, 200[1] charges (.035 min./charge)   =7,357 min.

Time to date unused slips:
20, 400 slips (.035 min./slip)   = 714 min.

Punching time:
200,000 charges (.0369 min./charge)   =7,380 min.

          15,451 min.

117

Analysis of a University Library

Minus exit dating time:
200,000 charges (.035 min./charge)   7,000 min.
                                                        8,451 min.
Money saved:
8,451 min. ($1.19/60 min.)   = $168

Form money saved:
20,400 charges ($.006/charge)   122
                                                       $290

[1] 10,200 are re-dated faculty charges

Before any significant reduction in exiting time can be realized, the
exit control and the charging operation will have to be separated.
The fastest charging system included in Study of Circulation Control
Systems requires 8 seconds to charge a book. The present method
requires approximately 15 seconds. It may seem that a savings of
7 seconds on each book would be a significant savings, but the
costs of the faster systems make the adoption of any of these systems prohibitively expensive.

If the exit control function was separated from the charging
function, it would require approximately 4 seconds, on the average,
for a person to pass through the exit control desks. To separate
the functions, a charging desk would have to be established at
another location. Three factors would guide the location of the charging desk: (1) to prevent congestion at the exit it should not be near
the exit control desks; (2) it should be convenient for the library
users; and (3) it should be located so that students are "motivated"
by its location to charge their books before they are ready to exit,
thus reducing crowding at peak times.

Perhaps the most advantageous location for the charging desk
would be on the second floor of the building near the stack entrance:
this is centrally located; it would eliminate the congestion and confusion in the lobby; it would not cause the students to wait until
exiting to charge books; and it would minimize the inconvenience to
the library user.

Relocation of the charging function would increase the cost
to the library, since a person would be required at both the charging desk and the exit control desk during the hours the library is

open. If the function was combined with some other function in the Circulation Department (e.g., sorting, tabbing charge slips), the additional cost could be minimized. There would also be some reduction in exit control time, and this would help defray the cost of maintaining the charging desk.

Conclusions:

It is believed that no significant improvements can be made in the present system without a prohibitively high cost. The recommended change is the separation of the charging function and the exit control function. Although it would increase costs, this change would relieve the congestion in the lobby without a decrease in service to library users. The combination of the two functions is the major cause of the congestion. In view of the fact that the library plans to establish an IBM system within a few years, a conversion to a new circulation system is not advisable. Only one system included in Study of Circulation Control Systems has a potential savings over the present system, and the monetary savings that the library would obtain in a few years does not justify converting to the system.

Eliminating pre-dating, eliminating punching, and dating charge slips at exit control will result in a small savings to the library. The changes will simplify the procedure as well as save money.

Results:

The circulation file was moved from the lobby to the second floor, making room for a charging desk separate from exit control. The length of the exit lines dropped sharply. Under the new system, peak period loads require only two exit control checkers compared to the four required formerly.

Because of the relatively small potential savings no change was made in the circulation procedure. This decision was also based on a desire to minimize any confusion created by the new exit control arrangement.

[1]George Fry & Associates, Study of Circulation Systems, Chicago: Library Technology Project of the American Library Association and the Council on Library Resources, Inc., 1961.

Investigation of the Cost of Periodical Replacement in the
Periodical Reading Room of the University Library

By: D. A. Wood, C. G. Uligian, R. E. Beck

Objective

The objective of this project is to investigate the cost of
periodical replacement in the Periodical Reading Room in order to
assess the feasibility of a closed stack operation for this room.

Background

The administration of periodicals in the University Library is
associated with the Circulation Department. The periodicals are
housed in a separate room known as the Periodical Reading Room
which contains some 3,800 titles. The separation of the periodical
function from other services rests on the assumption that more effective service may be given this way. [1] The Periodical Reading Room
contains only the current unbound issues of each periodical. The
room is open to the public, although the periodicals may not be
charged out.

Occasionally, the Periodical Reading Room assistant cannot
find all the issues of a periodical which are to be bound. The reasons for this are that the issue has never been received, that it has
been lost, or that it has been stolen from the library. This missing
issue has to be replaced at a cost to the library. The question asked by the library administration is, "Should we exert tighter control
over these periodicals by converting to a closed stack operation?"
By exerting this tighter control, the library feels it could eliminate
or at least minimize the replacement of missing issues. Therefore,
the deciding factor will be whether the annual cost of the proposed
closed stack system will be more economical than the annual cost
of replacing the missing periodicals.

Current Procedure

The Periodical Reading Room assistant searches for issues of
a periodical which is to be bound. If she cannot find all of the issues in the Periodical Reading Room, she looks further, first in the

120

stacks, and then in the current checklist to see if the issue has ever been received. If the issue has been received and she cannot find it, a replacement order is placed. On the average, the extra time spent as a result of the missing periodical (including the typing of a replacement order) is about one half hour. In order to determine the cost of the clerk's time, we will have to compute her effective hourly rate.

According to the method detailed in Memo on Effective Labor Costs, the effective hourly rate of the Periodical Reading Room assistant is $2.69 per hour. The cost of the one half hour of her time per order is

$2.69/hour x 1/2 hour/order = $1.35 per order

However, it was found that each order represented on the average 1.9 issues. Therefore, the cost per issue is

$1.35/order ÷ 1.9 issues/order = $0.71 per issue

The cost of the replacement form is calculated as follows:

$23.73 per 1000 or $0.02373/order

$0.02373/order ÷ 1.9 issues/order = $0.0125 per issue

After the replacement slip has been filled out, it is sent to an Order Department librarian, who sorts the various types of slips and gives the replacements to an Order Department assistant. The order librarian spends ten minutes per day sorting approximately fifty slips, of which ten are replacement orders for the Periodical Reading Room. The effective hourly rate of the order librarian is $7.94.

The cost of her time is

$$\frac{\$7.94}{\text{hour}} \text{ x } \frac{1 \text{ hour}}{60 \text{ min.}} \text{ x } \frac{10 \text{ min.}}{50 \text{ orders}} = \$0.0265 \text{ per order}$$

$0.0265/order ÷ 1.9 issues/order = $0.0139 per issue

The replacement order then goes to an Order Department assistant who has the responsibility of obtaining the desired periodicals. Since her operations are so varied, it is very hard to assign an average cost to a periodical replacement. Because of this difficulty, it was decided to approach this part of the problem from a macroscopic view point. Figures were obtained from the assistant's files

121

Analysis of a University Library

for the year 1963 that indicated what percentage of her work was done for the Periodical Reading Room, and of that work, what percentage was concerned with replacements. It was found that 90% of her work is concerned with shortages and replacements for the whole library system. Of these, 23.8% were orders from the Periodical Reading Room. Finally, of the orders from the Periodical Reading Room, 44% were orders strictly for replacements of lost periodicals.

The cost of the Order Department assistant's time is

$5,228   (her annual salary, including 12% fringe benefits)

x .90   (90% of her work is concerned with shortages or re-
$4,705   placements)

x .238   (23.8% of the above is for the P.R.R.)
$1,129   (assignable to replacement of shortages from the P.R.R.)

x .44   (44% of the above is replacement work)
$ 497   Cost of assistant's replacement labor

On the average there are 211 replacement orders per year

$\dfrac{\$ 497}{211} = \$2.36$ Cost of her labor per order

But since there are 1.9 issues per order

$\dfrac{\$ 2.36}{1.9} = \$1.24$ Cost of her labor assignable to each issue

Again, using the macroscopic point of view, the authors determined that each replacement order will result in 1.1 letters. The following postage costs are incurred:

56.0% of letters are domestic	@ $.05	= .028
30.6% of letters are European	@ .15	= .046
13.4% of letters are other foreign	@ .25	= .033
Average postage per letter		$0.107

Therefore, the average mailing cost per order is 1.1 x $.107= $.118

But again, there are 1.9 issues per order, so

$.118/1.9 = $.062 per issue for postage

The cost of the envelopes involved was found as follows:

$21.30 per 1000 or $0.02133 per envelope

$\dfrac{\$0.02123}{\text{envelope}} \times 1.1 \dfrac{\text{envelopes}}{\text{order}} = \$0.0234$ per order

There are 1.9 issues per order,

$$\frac{\$0.0234}{\text{order}} \div 1.9 \frac{\text{issues}}{\text{order}} = \$0.012 \text{ per issue}$$

As the orders are sent out, the assistant sends one part of the replacement order form to be filed in the current check list by a clerk, so that filled orders will be routed correctly back to her. Placing the pink slip in the current check list involves the following:

sorting 2 sec.

searching 29 sec.

filing 2 sec.

33 sec. or .55 minutes

Therefore, the cost per order for filing the extra slip in the current check list is

Effective hourly rate = $2.72 per hour

$$\frac{\$2.72}{\text{hour}} \times \frac{1 \text{ hour}}{60 \text{ min.}} \times \frac{.55 \text{ min.}}{\text{order}} = \$0.025 \text{ per order}$$

$$\frac{\$0.025}{\text{order}} \quad 1.9 \frac{\text{issues}}{\text{order}} = \$0.0132 \text{ per issue}$$

From the 1963 statistics it was found that the average cost of a issue replaced for the Periodical Reading Room was $1.535.

Once the order has been placed, the next operation is receiving the serial in the mail room. It is assumed that all serials are sent by first class mail. (Very rarely is a serial received by parcel post.) Two operations are performed by mailroom personnel. The first is the transporting of the first class mail bags from the loading dock to the first class mail sorting room. This transporting incurs a cost of $.001 per issue. The bags of mail are emptied and the mail sorted. The periodicals form one group of items sorted out from the mail bag. They are sorted alphabetically, and those with the pink shipping label are separated from those without. Sorting in the first class mail room takes .667 minutes per serial. Assuming an average effective wage of $1.25/hour, the cost incurred is

$$\frac{\$1.25}{\text{hour}} \times \frac{1 \text{ hour}}{60 \text{ min.}} \times \frac{.667 \text{ min.}}{\text{issue}} = \$0.0139 \text{ per issue}$$

Altogether, the cost incurred per issue for the handling and sorting in the mail room is

$.001 x $.0139 = $.0149 or $.015 per issue

123

Analysis of a University Library

Half of the replacement periodicals received in the mail room have the pink shipping label and thus go directly to the order librarian's assistant. The other half must go through the normal serial check-in procedure at the current check list. The operation at the current check list is as follows:

Sort	2 sec.
Search	29 sec.
Refile	10 sec.
Stamp	5 sec.
Place in interlibrary tote box	10 sec.
	56 sec. = .94 min.

However only one-half of the replacement serials are checked in the current check list, so the average cost per periodical is

$$\frac{\$2.72}{hour} \times \frac{1 \ hour}{60 \ min.} \times \frac{(1/2 \times .94) \ min.}{issue} = \$0.021 \ per \ issue.$$

The whole procedure just described is depicted in the following flow chart.

Summary of the Costs Incurred in Replacing a Periodical for the Periodical Reading Room

1.	P.R.R. staff time	$0.710 (per issue)
2.	Replacement form	.012
3.	Order librarian	.014
4.	Order assistant	1.240
5.	Postage	.062
6.	Envelope	.012
7.	Current checklist filing	.013
8.	Actual cost of issue	1.535
9.	Mail room handling & sorting	.015
10.	Current check list check-in	.021
		$3.634 (per issue)

Average total cost to replace an issue for the P.R.R. --$3.634
In terms of annual cost this would be:

211 orders per year
x1.9 volumes per order
400 volumes replaced x 3.634 = $1,454 per year

Cost of Periodical Replacement

It must be remembered that the value to the library of having a periodical on hand at all times has not been considered in this report.

In a closed stack operation, one would need a page to work when the clerk is not available. (This is a minimum requirement.) This amounts to 47 hours per week. Assuming $1.50 per hour pay rate, the annual cost of a closed stack operation is

$1.50 per hour x 1.19 Correction factor = $1.79 effective rate.

47 hours/week x $1.79/hour x 50 weeks/year = $4,207 per year.

Conclusions

During the year of 1963 orders for shortages and replacements in the Periodical Reading Room totaled two hundred and sixty-eight. Of the two hundred and sixty-eight orders, there were two hundred and thirty-seven separate titles. The present system in the Periodical Reading Room involves a selective closed stack system consisting of approximately ten titles. Since the replacements are spread over so many titles it does not seem likely that the disappearance of many issues could be prevented by a small increase in the size of the selective closed stack. The cost incurred by the present replacements does not seem to justify closing the stacks, since to do so would cost more than twice as much as the total cost of the replacements, at the present rate of replacement. Also, the four hundred issues lost per year represent only two percent of the issues held in the room.

Analysis of a University Library

Operational Flow Chart of the Serial Re-Acquisition Process

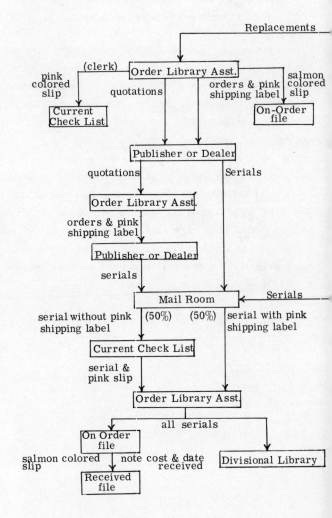

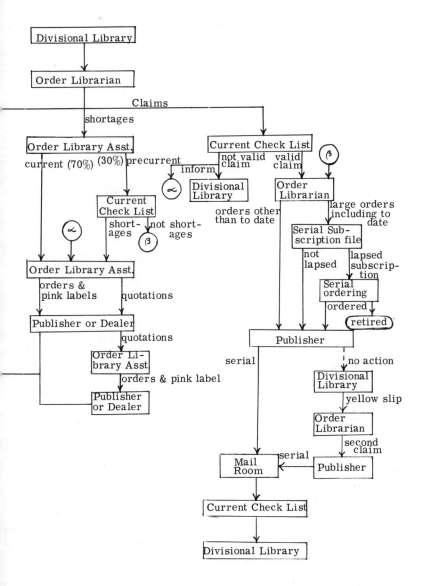

127

Analysis and Improvement of the Accounting System of the
Photoduplication Service

By: R. E. Beck, H. L. Benford, E. W. Deardorff

Objective

    The cost of information obtained from the library system for use in the library system can be measured in terms of time and money. The time and money spent in obtaining this information must be directly proportional to the significance of this information, since both resources are at a premium in any library system. Therefore, any library data collection system must be as efficient and effective as possible. The objective of this report was to investigate the accounting system in the Photoduplication Department of the University of Michigan Library in an attempt to "streamline" the system.

Background and Present System

    The Photoduplication Department furnishes several services to library patrons, including individuals, University departments, and outside business firms. These services include photostat, Xerox, microfilm, ozalid, embosograph, and microfilm-reader repair.

    The Photoduplication Service has no connection with or concern about the actual collection of money for work done, except for over-the-counter cash sales. Credit for work processed for University departments and outside business firms is assigned to the Photoduplication Department by the University Accounting Department. All transactions are noted in the monthly income statement prepared by Accounting, and a copy of the transaction is provided for Photoduplication. This copy serves as a final check to insure that credit was received for all work processed. Prices for the services provided are derived from cost analysis and through comparisons with the prices at similar establishments.

    The accounting system will be broken down into three parts: cash, University departments, and outside business firms. Appendix A illustrates the operations performed for each of these areas.

Cash:

Cash paid over-the-counter for processed work is put into the cash register, and the tape is given to the customer as a receipt. The second tape, inside the cash register, is checked against the money in the drawer. Each week, most of the cash is taken to the Administration Building and deposited with the cashier, who makes out a deposit slip for the amount deposited. This amount is entered in the ledger, and the deposit slip is filed. No job order is made out for this type of work, unless the customer wishes to pick up the processed work at a later time.

University Departments:

University departmental work differs considerably from cash sales. The Photoduplication Service receives interdepartmental requisitions (IDR) which describe the type of work to be done for the departments during the year. Some of the IDR's specify a limit on the total that a department can charge and the Photoduplication Service must therefore keep these departments' balances up to date in order to prevent them from overspending. When an order from a department arrives, the ledger must be checked in order to determine if there is a sufficient balance. If there is, a job order is made up in triplicate. The original is sent with the order while the second and third are filed alphabetically and numerically, respectively. The alphabetical file copy of the job order is the basis for the transfer voucher, which is subsequently prepared and sent to Accounting; this information is also entered in the ledger. The transfer voucher is processed by Accounting and given a voucher number. One copy is then returned to Photoduplication where the voucher number is posted in the ledger to assure that credit has been received. A further check is the receipt of the monthly income statement from Accounting, which lists all the transactions.

Outside Business:

The administrative procedure for outside business is similar to that for departmental work. No blanket or specified limits are involved, but the rest of the procedure is identical, with the exception of the use of an invoice instead of a transfer voucher. The invoice is prepared from the job order, and the same type of ledger posting occurs. After processing, Accounting returns a copy to Photoduplication, where the invoice number is posed to ensure proper credit. The monthly income statement again serves as an additional check. These systems were flow-charted and are presented below.

At the end of each month and year, a report is compiled which breaks down the sales by process (Xerox, microfilm, etc.) and by source (cash, departmental, and outside business). These statistics are obtained from the alphabetically-filed job orders. A separate adding machine tape is prepared and rechecked for each total; this is a very time-consuming process.

Proposed System

The general approach to this problem relied heavily upon the principle that the significance of any information should be directly proportional to the effort spent in collecting it. This means any duplication of information will be eliminated if possible. Any insignificant information such as subtotals, weekly totals, etc. will save time and money if eliminated. One can see that centralization of information in the ledger creates some duplication of information because such information is available from the job order files. The cost incurred in centralizing this information in the ledger is not commensurate with the benefits. The Committee on Internal Audit of the University was consulted, and the proposed system appears to meet all University requirements.

Cash

The information located in the cash sales section of the ledger is unnecessary. This information, which is needed for compiling reports, can be obtained easily by consulting the cash deposit slips in the file. The ledger, while not requiring much time, is unnecessary and therefore could be eliminated.

University Departments

Complete elimination of ledger entries for departmental work is not feasible since the retention of up-to-date balances for departments is necessary, and because a check must be made as to whether credit is received for work done. The system, however, could be simplified. An easier way of checking departmental balances, if there is a specified limit, would be to attach a card to the original IDR. As each order for the department was processed, the figure giving the remaining balance could be updated; no other data would be necessary. A quick glance at the card would then suffice to determine the balance available.

The check on receipt of credit for work done could be done more easily by using a two-column ledger; then, when the vouchers had been returned with transfer voucher numbers assigned by Accounting, these numbers would be entered in the second column beside the appropriate job order number. A visual scanning would then indicate those job order numbers for which no credit had been received, and the situation could then be corrected.

Another possible method for ensuring that credit has been received requires no ledger at all. It involves the use of a tracing number which would be placed on the transfer voucher and a copy of the job order. Then, when the transfer vouchers were returned, they would be scanned for missing numbers, a missing number would indicate that credit had not been received, and the situation could then be remedied.

Outside Business

The elimination of ledger entries for outside business is possible, but it does not ensure that credit is received. A two-column ledger similar to that discussed above could be used, with the following addition: work done for businesses in foreign countries should have the country, customer, and amount noted in the ledger. This is desirable as an aid in tracking down problems which sometimes occur in these cases.

The flow-charts of the proposed systems, which follow, can be used to compare present and proposed systems.

Conclusions

The weekly cash entries in the ledger should be discontinued because (1) the cash deposit slips which are obtained from the Cashier provide all necessary information; (2) an unnecessary duplication is eliminated; and (3) some time will be saved.

Ledger entries for departmental work should be eliminated,

131

except for a two-column ledger containing entries for job order number and transfer voucher number. Job order numbers for which no transfer voucher numbers are given indicate that credit has not been received. The numerically-filed job order can be consulted in order to remedy the problem. This method of ensuring credit was chosen over the tracing-number method because this latter method would require extensive sorting of the returned transfer vouchers; a time consuming process.

Departmental balances formerly kept in the ledger would be kept on cards attached to the IDR's. These should be consulted before an order is processed to determine if there is a sufficient balance, and then updated with the new balance after the order is compiled.

Ledger entries for outside work should also be minimized. A two-column ledger, for job-order number and corresponding invoice number, should be set up. In cases of foreign businesses, the customer, country, and amount should be entered along with the job order number. When the job orders are returned and invoice numbers posted beside corresponding job orders, any job order not credited to Photoduplication may be noted.

Present Systems

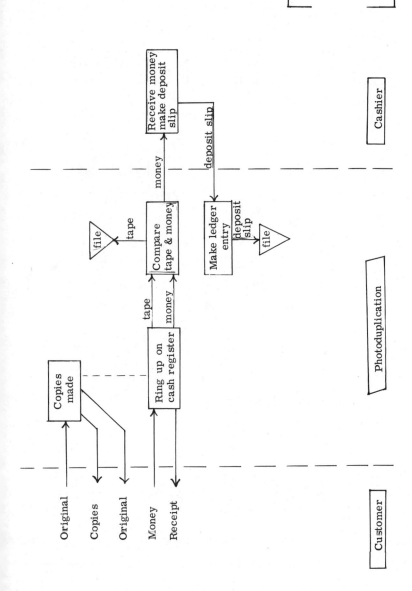

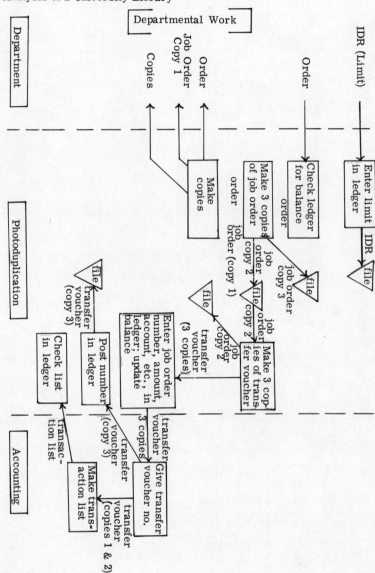

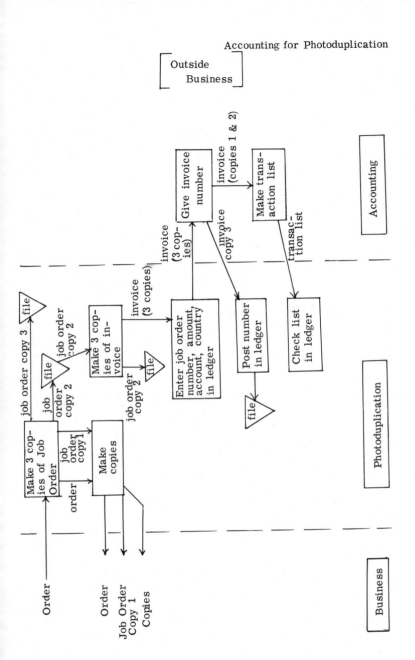

135

Departmental Work

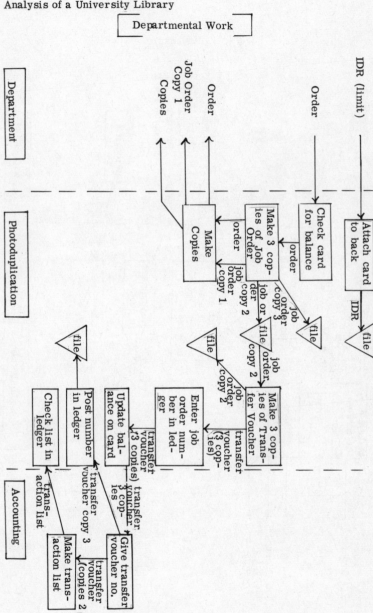

A Photo Copier Accounting System for the Library Photo-duplication Department

By: R. E. Beck, M. C. Drott

Objective:

The purpose of this study was to design an accounting system and any necessary forms to monitor the performance of the new coin-operated Dennison photo-copiers.

Background:

The library recently purchased nine Dennison Model C-O photo-copiers for approximately $2,700 each. These copiers will be located in various libraries in the system to provide a coin-operated, self-service copying facility for patrons.

Each machine will be serviced daily. This servicing will consist of collecting the money and checking the supplies. There are three types of supplies involved: paper (one roll makes about 650 copies), toner (a bottle lasts for about 1,000 copies), intensifier (one bottle will last for over 12,000 copies). These supplies will be replaced in unit quantities (i.e. one whole roll or bottle at a time).

Each machine is equipped with two counters. One counter records the number of dimes put into the machine, the other the total number of copies made. There are two factors which can account for any difference in these meters. First, each machine has a key switch which allows the machine serviceman to make test copies without inserting a dime. Second, one of the copiers is equipped with a cost controller, a device consisting of six additional counters each corresponding to a special key. These keys are available to University departments and allow them to make copies on credit. Each month each department will be billed at the standard rate of $.10 per copy for all copies shown on its special meter. If this service proves popular, cost controllers may be installed on other machines.

All meters operate sequentially and cannot be reset. The coin boxes accept only dimes and do not make change. The librarian in charge of the area where the machine is located is given a small

137

amount of cash ($2.00) to make refunds to customers who lose money in the copiers.

The accounting system should keep track of monies collected and supplies expended. It should account for the labor of servicing the machines, the cost of the service contracts to be purchased annually, the cost of repair parts, and refunds. There should be a running record of the amortization of machine costs. And there should be sufficient data to compare the efficiency of each machine with that of the other machines in the system.

Analysis:

There are several general principles which should be observed. First, cash should be carefully controlled. Second, data collection should be as easy as possible. Third, the number of forms generated should be kept to a minimum. Fourth, performance data should be in an easy-to-evaluate form.

Since cash will be collected daily, a special collection record was devised. As a check, daily receipts will be compared with the coin meter reading. To minimize effort, the slip has a record of the previous coin meter reading. The use of the slip is as follows: the serviceman takes from the machine a pad of cash slips which already have the machine number on them. He records the current coin meter reading in the "Previous" box. This slip is placed in the coin box, after the slip placed there the day before and the cash have been removed. On the slip from the day before the current coin meter reading is entered in the space marked "Present". The slip is then dated and signed and placed in a bag with the cash. At the office the cash is counted and the amount entered in the appropriate space. This figure can easily be compared to the difference between the two meter readings. It is, of course, a good practice to have the cash counted by a different person than the one who collected it, although this does not need to be done every time. These slips are then filed to be totaled at the end of the month.

A record of supplies must be kept as the materials are put in the machine. There is, however, no need to tabulate these figures daily. The cost sheet (below) was developed to be kept in the machine and collected monthly. This data sheet is used as follows: At the beginning of the month the serviceman fills in the blanks at the top of the page and enters the meter readings in the "Previous" boxes. Each time the machine is serviced, the quantity of each type of material is entered opposite the appropriate date. At the end of the month each meter reading is entered in the "Present" box. All supplies are totaled and each "Copy" record is calculated. The cash slips are totaled and entered in the appropriate space. The "Key Meter" readings provide information for departmental billing and the "Credit" blank. Supply costs are calculated and entered in the appropriate space. This cost sheet is then filed in a ring binder by machine and date. This binder provides a quick summary of the month's activities. A master sheet which contains the total supplies and copies for all machines is also prepared and filed. This system minimizes record keeping, since the serviceman's daily record becomes automatically a part of the permanent record. There is also a safety factor which prevents loss of the first of the month readings since both the previous month's record and the sheet currently in the machine contain this data.

The final document needed for this system is a permanent cash ledger. This ledger has three main columns; income, current expense, and unamortized expense.

```
┌─────────────────────────────────────────────────────────┐
│                    Cash Record                          │
│  Machine_____        Date_____          │
│                                                         │
│            Coin Meter                                   │
│  Present  ┌─────────────┐                               │
│  Previous ├─────────────┤        Cash $_____         │
│  Copies   └─────────────┘                               │
│                                                         │
│                       Collected by_____          │
│                                                         │
└─────────────────────────────────────────────────────────┘
```

Entries are of the monthly summary type as shown below. The income entries come from the cost sheets discussed previously. Current expenses come from the cost sheet and from other billings.

Analysis of a University Library

Copier Cost Machine

Machine_____ Location_____ Date_____

Date	Paper	Toner	Intens.	Test Copies	Master Meter		
1					Present		
2					Previous		
					Copies		
3							
4					Coin Meter		
5					Present		
6					Previous		
					Copies		
7							
8					Key Meter Total _____		
9							
10					Copies not accounted for_____		
11							
12					Sales		
13					Cash $_____		
14					Credit $_____		
15					Income $_____		
16							
17					Expenses		
18					Paper $ _____		
19					Toner _____		
20					Intens. _____		
21					Test C. _____		
22					Total $ _____		
23							
24							
25							
26							
27							
28							
29							
30							
31							
Totals							

Key Meters	A1	A2	A3	B1	B2	B3
Present						
Previous						
Copies						

Note that refunds are charged as an expense when the money is given to the librarian. Labor is charged by charging the total time evenly to the several machines. The net profit or loss is used to adjust the unamortized expense column. Charges which apply to several months (such as a year's service contract) are charged directly to this column. Again a master record is kept which summarizes the activities of all the machines.

Sample Ledger Entries

Machine 19311

Copies		Current Income		Current Expense	Unamortized Expense
					$2,500.00
			October 1966		
1312	Cash	$ 77.70	Supplies	$ 76.38	
	Credit	53.50	Labor	35.00	
		$131.20	Parts	8.50	Profit 11.32
				$119.88	$2488.68
			November 1966		
1057	Cash	$ 60.70	Supplies	$ 83.22	
	Credit	45.00	Labor	35.00	
		$105.70	Refund	2.00	Loss 14.52
				$120.22	Service 77.00
					$2580.20

Results:

The above recommendations were adopted as listed. It was found that there was some difficulty in keeping the cash record slips, and so the department devised a simple record sheet on which the data from the slips is recorded. This sheet is filed in the binder with the cost sheets.

Increased Seating in the Undergraduate Library: A Study in
Effective Space Utilization

By: J. J. Cook

The objective of this project was to increase the seating capacity of the Undergraduate Library Building without reducing the collection sizes or limiting the service and operating efficiency.

The Undergraduate Library Building is a relatively new facility
on the University of Michigan campus opened in January of 1958.
Although named the Undergraduate Library, the facility is open to
all university students, staff, and faculty. The rectangular, five-
floor structure has space allocation for (1) the Undergraduate Library
on the basement, first, and half of the second floor, (2) the Education Library on the remaining half of the second floor, (3) the Engineering-Transportation Library on the third and part of the fourth
floor, (4) an art print study gallery and a machine room, which contains heating and air-conditioning equipment, on the remaining portion of the fourth floor.

Because the building contains other libraries besides the Undergraduate Library, hereafter UGL will be used in reference to the
facility and "Undergraduate Library" in reference to that particular
library.

The UGL is an open-stack study facility. A previous study of
student behavior showed that one-third of the daytime users of the
facility solely use personal books or notebooks while in the library.
The central location of the facility on the main campus makes it accessible to students with one or two hours free between classes.

Among the services offered by the UGL are reserve and open
stack collections, reference aids, periodicals, record collection and
audio room, typing rooms, photocopying, microfilm viewing, a multi-
purpose room, and a student lounge with refreshment vending machines.

The environment created by the original design was uncrowded,

142

colorful and attractive, and the furniture comfortable. Wide aisles for main traffic and traffic within the stacks were provided. Numerous lounging areas suited the purpose of the interior design, which was to create such an inviting environment that students would enjoy using the facilities. The UGL was so successful in drawing students that by 1964 periodic severe overcrowding occured. During examination periods particularly, students were studying in the aisles, hallways, and stairways.

Definition of the Problem

Library overcrowding and the associated high noise level within the library became a major problem to the UGL. Less serious problems were also being experienced: more office space was needed for the Undergraduate Library and for the Engineering-Transportation Library to meet the increased workload and staffing requirements. The rare book room associated with the Engineering-Transportation Library had become too small for the functions performed in it. The reference librarians' desks in the Undergraduate Library were in an area with very high traffic and noise. The stacks arrangement on the shared second floor made it difficult for the users to discriminate between the collections of the Undergraduate Library and the Education Library. Selective "weeding" and controlled growth of collection sizes had prevented major problems from arising in shelf space, but a modest increase in shelving was desired to maintain flexibility.

A preliminary study was initiated. The study was to consist of three main units: (A) an earlier sample of student behavior was to be studied; (B) samples of student preference of furniture and student use of lounge areas were to be made; and (C) the various types of furniture arrangements in study areas were to be measured for guidelines in spacing and evaluated for effectiveness.

The sample of student behavior did not provide any information relevant to the objective of this project. It did permit those who were involved with the project to gain an awareness of certain characteristics of the clientele using the library and its facilities.

A sample of furniture preference was made by taking a count of seats occupied as a percent of seats available for each type of furniture. Data were collected randomly throughout each day for a number of days. These data were then stratified into two groups: near capacity and low usage. The data for the near capacity group were disregarded, since in this situation it is unlikely that each person chooses the type of furniture he prefers. The low usage group was further stratified by types of furniture.

For example: Individual desks 85 seats available - 57% occupied

Four-man tables 108 seats available - 40% occupied

Lounge areas   67 seats available - 13% occupied

Spiders*   80 seats available - 52% occupied

The low usage data were used because there is a high probability that, with a wide assortment of seating to choose from, each person seated is at the type of furniture of his choice.

The results of this sample indicated that preferences were in the following order: first, individual desks or spider areas; second, shared four-man desks; and last, a chair or settee in the lounge areas.

It was suspected that lounge areas were not as effective study areas as those with tables, spiders and individual desks. A study of lounge areas bears this out. A sample indicated that the average person seated in a lounge area uses 2.13 seats. The most common behavior was the use of one seat for sitting and a second for a footrest. Occasionally a third seat was used for books, or, in cool weather, overcoats.

Selected arrangements were measured to determine existing aisle width guidelines. Because the UGL contained nearly 1,500 seats and just over 1,000 sections of shelving it was too expensive to measure every aisle. Typical areas were selected and measured to determine existing spacing guidelines, and diagrams were drawn recording the measurements. An evaluation of these guidelines will be discussed later in connection with the setting of new standards.

---

* Spider is the name coined for units consisting of a tall dividing panel with a desk attached to each side of the panel. These consisted of groupings of four, six, eight and ten seats.

Following the preliminary studies the librarians and staff were queried regarding the changes they would desire if new arrangements of furniture and stacks were to be designed. Those questioned pointed out that study areas near entrances to the floors tended to be social centers and index tables were being used for studying rather than for consulting indexes. Other personal preferences were also stated.

After the preliminary studies, means were sought to solve problems and satisfy desires for improvements. A simulation was performed to test the existing guidelines for furniture arrangements and to aid in developing new guidelines. Two or three areas were chosen as typical of basic floor plans. The furniture in these areas was maneuvered into various arrangements to simulate a new situation. Activities common to the areas were performed to test the effectiveness of the new arrangements.

Simulation Process

The simulation process, for example, involved tables arranged so that some people were seated back-to-back. Our test person entered the area and took a seat. Then, a second person entered the area and found out how easily one gained access to another seat and how comfortably one could study in the seat back-to-back with the first person. This test was repeated with varying distances between pieces of furniture and with the furniture in varying arrangements. Various aisle widths were tested by having two people walk through an arrangement, a person push a book cart through, and a person or two walk through when a book cart had been left in the aisle.

Concepts in Furniture Arrangement

Several concepts were developed from the simulation process, particularly in table and desk arrangements: (1) Small individual desks, when not bolted to the floor, are best placed against a wall. If free-standing, they tend to get moved either into aisle space or too close to the other furniture. (2) Two tables placed tightly together, end-to-end, necessitate only two access aisles, one on each end of the arrangement and one through the center. The same principle applies to three tables. When the tables are placed end-to-end, a significant amount of floor space is saved. (3) Simple geometric designs tend to take up the least floor space. (4) Spiders, with their high dividing panels, are excellent units to break a large study area into smaller, more appealing, and more attractive study areas.

Rigid principles are not feasible for dealing with the problem of designing arrangements for study areas. Library furnishings are so varied that what may apply to one style of tables, desks, and chairs may not apply to another style. Some general concepts are useful, however, in developing principles for one's particular situation.

A feasibility study was initiated in the form of a layout project to determine if the principles developed from the simulation could substantially aid in increasing seating in the UGL. Making a layout is analogous to setting up an office desk. Say that a person has an office desk, with a top measuring three by five feet. On this desk he wants to place a basket for incoming papers and another basket for outgoing papers, a lamp, a small clock, a pen and pencil holder, a desk pad, a framed picture, and four reference books important to his job. One does not simply start piling each of the objects he wishes onto the desk. Rather, he arranges the objects in terms of convenience. The desk pad goes directly in front of him where he will most use it. The pen and pencil holder will also be in easy reach, as will the incoming and outgoing-paper baskets. The reference books are not used constantly and therefore are placed conveniently but less accessibly than the other objects. Farthest from reach are the picture and clock, as they only need to be seen. The lamp is located to provide the best lighting for the work space. Once the objects have been placed for convenience and function, one will probably stand back and judge his arrangement for its pleasing appearance. With a few more adjustments in his arrangement he finally has what he feels is a functional, convenient, and attractive desk arrangement, and he goes to work.

Basically the same procedure is followed in designing a layout. The room or rooms with which one wants to work are measured. A suitable scale (e.g. 1/2 or 1/4 inch representing a foot) is chosen to make a basic floor plan of workable size. Then a sheet of layout paper (similar to graph paper) is cut such that it is a little larger than the outer borders of what will be the basic floor plan. The basic floor plan is drawn in pencil. This plan represents an empty room and is similar to a blueprint. It views the building as if there were no roof and as if one were looking down from above.

When one is certain that no permanent detail has been missed (drinking fountain, pillars, doorways, etc.) a gloss tape or ink can be drawn over the pencil design. This operation "fixes" the basic floor plan, preparing it for use and, later, blueprinting. This plan will show any constraining objects: windows, stairways, doorways, pillars, heat and air vents, built-in cabinets, etc. Returning to our analogy, one finds this similar to the empty desk top with which one begins.

When the basic floor plan has been completed, something must be devised to represent the desks, tables, cabinets, files, stacks and other movable objects which are to be placed in the room or building. For this, art paper of various colors works well. Colors are chosen to represent different classes of furniture and equipment. For example, blue for stacks, gray for file cabinets, green for tables, red for desks, etc. Paper templates are cut to scale and used for the basic floor plan. The templates represent the size and the shape of the physical objects to be placed in the room or rooms.

Just as the edge of the desk top is a limit in arranging a desk, the outer walls indicated in the basic floor plan are the binding limits to a room arrangement. The physical objects on a desk are maneuvered to create the most functional, convenient, and attractive arrangement. Similarly, the templates are maneuvered to achieve the same objectives on the floor plan and ultimately in the room.

The advantages of layout design versus physical changes are many: (a) flexibility, because an infinite array of designs can be drawn from one basic floor plan; (b) conceptualability, because by visualizing the whole plan it is easier to see the relationships of the parts to the whole; (c) ease, because one is moving templates rather than physical objects.

Analysis of a University Library

An important factor in making the layout technique successful is the detail of the basic floor plan. Extensive detailing is necessary because the layout is an orthographic projection (a "top view"). Detailing prevents such occurrances as tables placed in doorways or against drinking fountains, stacks passing through pillars, and file cabinets blocking heat vents.

The concepts developed through investigation and simulation are implemented in the process of making layouts. Templates are placed on the basic floor plan representing the existing arrangement. These are then maneuvered into the various arrangements developed through simulation; but now the whole room can easily be re-arranged rather than only a small portion. Various arrangements are tested to find those which provide the greatest gains in additional seating, shelving, and work space.

When the most desirable arrangement has been designed the templates are "fixed" into position by "double-stick" tape. The adhesive on both sides of the tape holds the templates tightly on the paper. If more than one arrangement is to be designed, as with the UGL project, a sheet of clear plastic (cellulose acetate) is placed over the basic floor plan. The templates are maneuvered on the plastic and later "fixed" to the plastic. The plastic sheet may then be removed for later use or blueprinting. A new sheet of plastic is placed over the basic floor plan and another arrangement may be designed. Re-use of a single basic floor plan saves time and supply costs.

When one is working with movable furniture, guidelines may be set by the simulation process. These guidelines may then be used when working with layouts. Shelving tends to be relatively immobile and any attempt at simulation would be tedious and time consuming. A study was performed to determine what stack aisle widths might be suitable for the UGL. The study consisted of two elements: stack aisles were measured in other divisional libraries on the University campus; librarians were asked if they felt that the aisles were too wide, too narrow or suitable for their particular library and if there were any problems encountered with their stack arrangement(s). The results of the study indicated that (1) 36" to 42" aisles were most desirable and (2) lighting arrangements may have to be modified when stack arrangements are changed.

The original design of the UGL had generously provided 54" aisles. Considerable floor space could be added to study areas if a means of narrowing stack aisles could be devised for the UGL. As was suspected, a major constraint was that the lighting in the UGL was designed to provide light in the center of each aisle. Decreasing the aisle widths in the arrangements on the layout indicated that some aisles would have a sharp decrease in lighting. The reason for this situation is that, periodically, stacks would be located directly under a row of flourescent lights.

A solution other than modification of the lighting was found. Ranges of shelving can be placed perpendicular to light rows rather than parallel. Further study indicated that in the UGL a 90° shift in the stack arrangements would not significantly affect the aisle lighting. Various layouts were designed to implement the findings and considerable floor space was freed for use as study areas.

Stack aisles were designed to be 39 inches wide. This dimension was within the desired range of 36 to 42 inches. The 39 inch aisle width was chosen because at that width stack arrangements aligned with the pillars in the rooms. Aisle widths less than or greater than 39 inches would create arrangements having pillars blocking some of the aisles.

Another means of conserving floor space was used in the UGL. In the stack areas the cross aisles were reduced in number and increased in size:
Original:

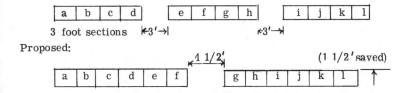

3 foot sections

Proposed:

149

Other considerations necessary in designing shelving layouts are as follows: (a) the type and size of the collection, (b) the style of shelving, (c) the amount of traffic anticipated in the stack area, (d) the type of lighting and lighting arrangement, (e) fire regulations, (f) the type and dimensions of book carts to be used, (g) the amount of supervision necessary, (h) the desired or necessary traffic patterns within and through the stack area, and (i) the maximum permissible floor loading. If deadend aisles are a necessity, the ranges of shelving should be only six to nine feet long and the aisles should be wider.

Library stacks can serve more functions than simply book storage. They also function as visual dividers and sound dampeners. In the UGL all three functions of shelving were utilized. As sound dampeners, they were used to advantage by arranging a few ranges near the main stairway on the heavily traveled basement floor. On the first floor they were placed to dampen sound between the catalog-reference area and the study areas. Wherever study areas were near high traffic, shelving was used to minimize visual and audial distractions. However, there are some situations where close supervision is necessary or desirable, and stacks, if improperly placed, would act detrimentally as visual dividers.

When designing layouts, one must be flexible. Libraries are not static but rather dynamic in nature. Resources are continually changing in the library. Collection sizes and content grow and change to meet changing needs, staffing changes, budgets grow or decline, clientele changes and occasionally the physical facility is changed. Precedent, a static influence, does not necessarily make things right or best. Continual re-evaluation is an essential element in meeting changing demands and new situations. Almost any additions to an existing facility will require compromise. Aisle widths may have to be reduced, office areas may encroach upon reading areas, a new design may appear crowded and unaesthetic. One of the hardest jobs of the librarian is to evaluate the additions.

UGL Proposed Layout (General)

Various arrangements of stacks were designed with the adoption of the 90° shift and reduced aisle widths. Stack areas were centralized on each floor and stacks arrangements were proposed as noise dampeners near entranceways on high traffic floors. An exception to the 90 degree shift is the west area of the main floor where the stacks were left in their former positions to cut down on the transfer of noise between the offices and the study area and to minimize traffic in the office area. The peripheral study and service areas were then designed.

Proposed Layout - 1st Floor

To resolve the traffic and noise problem in the reference areas, the reference/catalog area was moved from the alcove and placed in the center-front of the main floor. The reference desks were placed adjacent to the catalog with traffic flow designed to go in any direction through the catalog area without having to pass through the reference area first. Placement of the reference area was designed to make the reference librarians' jobs significantly easier and provide better reference service. Layout design placed reference librarians in the center of all activities common to their job. For example, previously the reference librarians had to cross a main traffic aisle to give students assistance with some of the reference aids. The new design placed the librarians adjacent to or near the catalog, indices, reserve notebooks, periodical lists, clipping file, reference collections, and other reference aids. Two offices were proposed for the vacated alcove.

2nd Floor

Confusion in discriminating the Undergraduate Library collection from the Education Library collection was eliminated by the new stacks arrangement. The two collections were each centralized and then divided by placing a study area between them.

4th Floor

Various alternatives were considered for enlarging the Rare Book Room. It was determined by the Engineering-Transportation librarian that a seldom-used portion of the collection on the fourth floor could be removed. After these stacks were removed, the Rare Book Room was moved to a more desirable portion of the fourth floor and enlarged. Also the stacks which were to remain were rearranged, and more study space was provided.

By applying the preceding concepts and principles an increase
of nearly 400 seats was attained in the new layout design of the UGL.

Proposed Layout (General)

Most lounge furniture was removed and the remaining furniture
was arranged so that it did not interfere with study areas. Spiders
were placed to create study areas of relatively equal size. Individual desks were placed against walls wherever possible in order to
avoid the expense of bolting them to the floor. Tables were arranged
in sets of two or three, end-to-end, wherever it seemed feasible
to the librarian in charge. Aisle and furniture-spacing guidelines
to the minimum necessary to continue common activities. All new
tables added had eye-height dividers to give the feeling of individual seating and were integrated with other types of seating rather
than concentrated in particular areas.

Result of Changes

The implementation of the proposed layouts resulted in
an increase in seating capacity from 1483 to 1877. The library
had a more professional appearance and experienced a noticeable decrease in student socializing. Although there were more users, a
quieter, more studious atmosphere prevailed.

Implementing Changes

Sufficient financial resources were available to implement the
layout changes on all five floors of the UGL. All changes were accomplished during the summer months of 1965. Had the financial resources not been available the changes could have been effected over
a longer period. That is, the complete layout design could be viewed
as a program, to be developed in stages, rather than solely as one
large project. The changes could have been implemented one floor
at a time, as budgeting permitted with no loss to the overall objectives and little disturbance of the relationships desired between each
of the floors, book collections, study areas, and services.

Final Remarks

During the process of laying out a given area one invariably con-
fronts a multitude of ideas for equipment and facilities. The layouts
presented represent an attempt to retain as much existing equipment

and furniture as possible, except for lounge furniture. The layouts were meant to satisfy the needs and desires of the library staff, to give the students better service, and to increase the over-all seating capacity of the library.

Ideal Arrangement for Convenience

The ideal situation, in terms of individual convenience is to create a system comprised solely of individual desks. But an individual desk and chair consume much more floor space per person than does a 4-man 4' x 6' table. As a compromise, it was recommended that all new tables purchased be equipped with eye-height dividers to create 4 individual study spaces.

In terms of cost, the UGL must initially pay $76 per seat to provide an individual desk and chair; it costs $58 per seat for a four-man 4' x 6' table with a divider which produces cubicles 2' x 3', the dimensions of an individual desk; and it costs $46 per seat for a four-man 4' x 6' study table without dividers or partitions, the type of table the UGL had when the project was initiated.

Spider arrangements originally were not considered to be fully effective because, at times, they separated only two or three tables from a much larger group. The proposed layouts were to utilize spiders to break the seating up into equal visual areas, as well as to give more individual seating.

Seating and Furniture Data - Undergraduate Library

	Tables		Desks		Spider Seats		Total Table Seats		Lounge Seats		Total Seating	
Basement												
Present	47		41		75		304		79		383	
Proposed		79		79		56		451		37		488
First Floor												
Present	35		15		61		216		91		307	
Proposed		50		34		54		288		29		317
Second Floor												
Present	42		34		64		266		120		386	
Proposed		87		51		57		456		37		493
Third Floor												
Present	47		21		48		257		93		350	
Proposed		76		37		58		399		14		413

Analysis of a University Library

Seating and Furniture Data (continued)

	Tables	Desks	Spider Seats	Total Table Seats	Lounge Seats	Total Seating
Fourth Floor						
Present	8	15	0	47	10	57
Proposed	26	36	16	156	10	166
Totals						
Present	179	126	248	1090	393	1483
Proposed	318	237	241	1750	127	1877

	Actual Seating	Percent Change	Preferred Seating*	Percent Change	New Tables Needed	New Desks Needed	New Chairs Needed
			Effect of Layout Changes				
Basement							
Present	383		336				
Proposed	488	27.4%	466	38.7%	32	38	166
First Floor							
Present	307		253				
Proposed	317	3.3%	300	18.6%	15	19	79
Second Floor							
Present	386		314				
Proposed	493	28%	471	50%	45	17	197
Third Floor							
Present	350		295				
Proposed	413	18%	405	37.3%	29	16	132
Fourth Floor							
Present	57		51				
Proposed	166	191%	160	214%	18	21	93
Totals							
Present	1483		1249				
Proposed	1877	26.5%	1802	44.3%	139	111	667

* Preferred seating represents functional seat availability. The number of preferred seats is a good indicator of the number of patrons
which can actually be accommodated. As shown earlier in the
report, people tend to use 2.13 lounge seats per person for themselves and their belongings, making lounge seats 40% effective.
Preferred seating consists of: table seats + individual seats + spider
seats + (.40 x lounge seats).

Summary of Changes: Basement

Shelving was consolidated in the central floor area with a reduction in the number of access aisles. Ranges of shelving were
lengthened to reduce the number of cross-aisles. Several ranges

were located to act as a noise buffer between study areas and the heavily-used student coffee lounge.

One lounge area was retained at the foot of the front stairway. This area is in harmony with the activities common to this area. Additionally, a generous aisle was provided between the stairway and the rooms for the blind.

Closely spaced individual desks and tables placed end-to-end resulted in additional seating accommodations. Spiders were rearranged and some moved to other floors.

Summary of Changes: First Floor

The reference area and areas containing reference aids were consolidated into a central area.

Stack arrangements buffer study areas and offices from the busy lobby.

Indices were accommodated on special long-legged tables with index shelves.

A single lounge area was retained for newspaper and current periodical display and use.

Summary of Changes: Second Floor

Stack areas for the Education Library and the Undergraduate Library were consolidated in the central floor area and separated by a study area.

An enlarged and more suitable charging and closed reserve area was provided for the Education Library.

Spider placement provides more equalized study areas. The elimination of most lounges and stacks consolidation provided additional seating space.

Summary of Changes: Third Floor

Rearrangement of stacks into a single central area provided added space for seating.

Additional work space and office areas were provided. Added seating is primarily in the form of divided four-man tables.

Maintenance of a central theme in stack and study area arrangements reflects the individuality of this library.

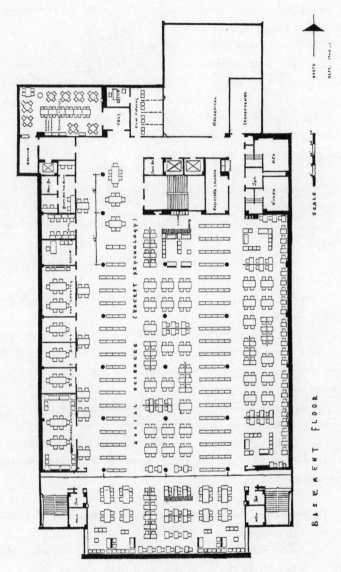

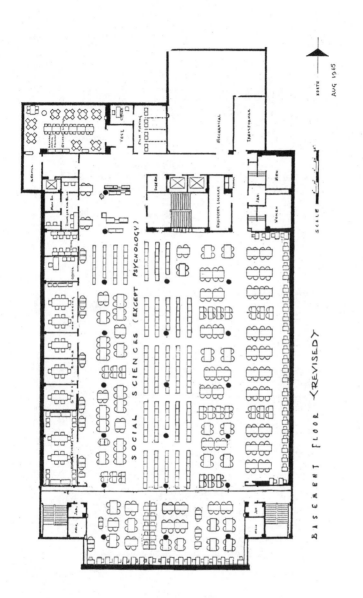

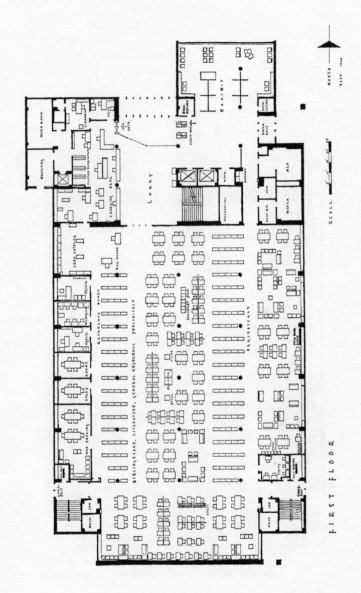

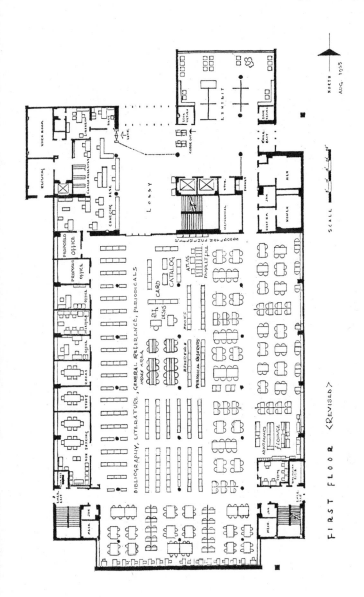

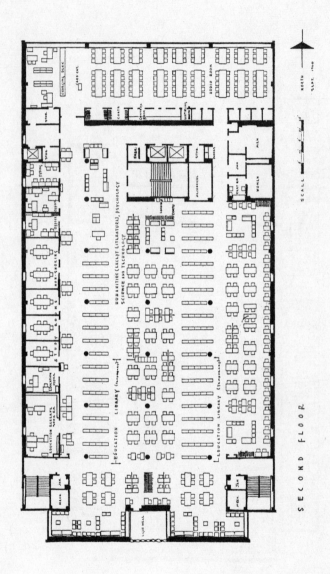

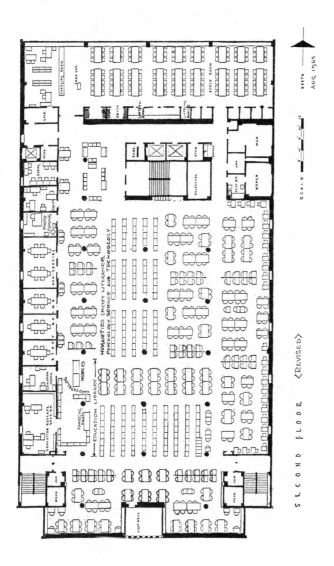

SECOND FLOOR (REVISED)

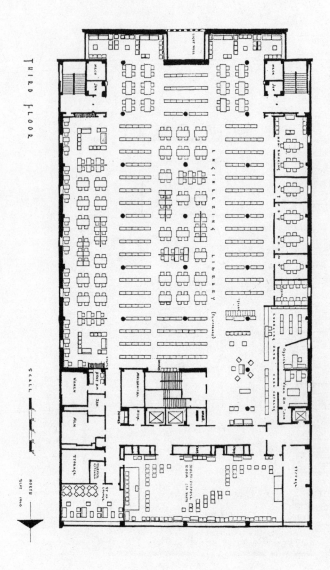

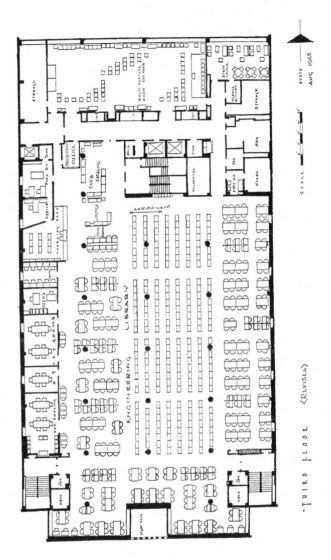

Analysis of a University Library

Summary of Changes: Fourth Floor

Seating space was greatly increased through a decision to eliminate many sections of shelving.

Change-over costs were minimized by retaining stacks spacing and orientation.

Color and variety in study areas was added by spider placement.

The enlarged Rare Book room was located so as not to disturb studying patrons.

All circulation and reference activities were previously centralized on the third floor by a merger of the Engineering and Transportation Libraries.

The office is used for file storage and special projects and research.

University of Michigan
Undergraduate Library Layout Project

Summary Sheet

	Present	Proposed	Gain	% Gain
Seating:				
Basement	383	488	105	27. 4%
First Floor	307	317	10	3. 3%
Second Floor	386	493	107	28. 0%
Third Floor	350	413	63	18. 0%
Fourth Floor	57	166	109	191. 0%
Totals	1483	1877	394	Overall Gain: 26. 6%

Stacks: (Number of 3 foot sections)				
Basement	158	164	6	3. 8%
First Floor	156 1/2	176	19 1/2	12. 5%
Second Floor	158	168	10	6. 3%
Third Floor	241	251	10	4. 1%
Fourth Floor	298	197	-101	-33. 9%
Totals	1011 1/2	956	-55 1/2	-5. 5%

Changes:	Double-faced Stacks	Table Seats	Desks	Spider Seats	Lounge Seats
Basement	6	128	38	-19	-42
First Floor	19 1/2	60	19	- 7	-62
Second Floor	10	180	17	- 7	-83
Third Floor	10	116	16	10	-79
Fourth Floor	-101	72	21	16	0
Total Inventory Change	- 55 1/2	556	111	- 7	-266

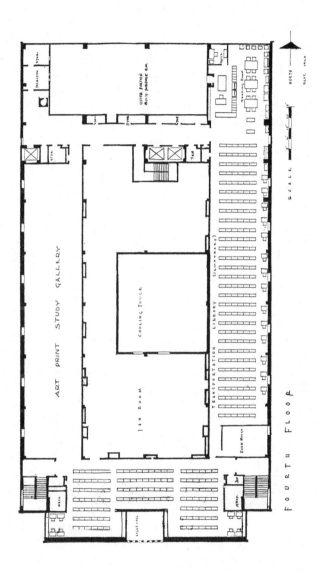

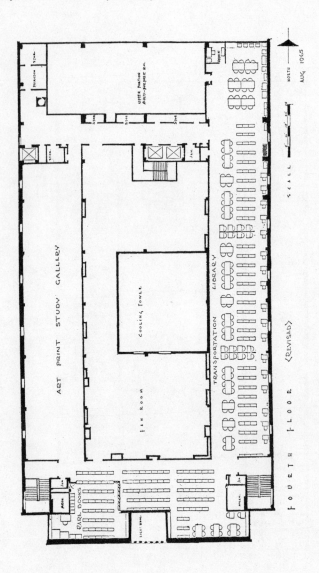

Improvement In

Reference Area Layout

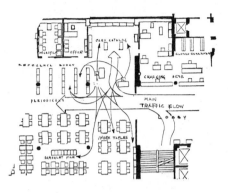

ORIGINAL

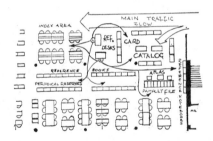

PROPOSED

The original layout shows the congestion in the reference area. Reference materials are scattered and traffic may interrupt reference work. The revision consolidates reference materials. Librarians are out of the traffic area, yet in a central, easily accessible position. Shelves screen the reference area from study areas.

167

5-3 inch Stack
Sections
(Double-Faced)

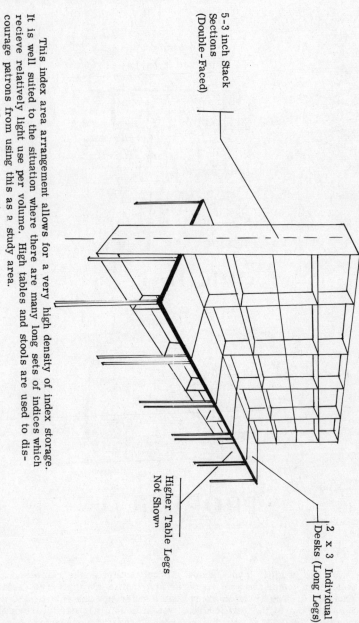

This index area arrangement allows for a very high density of index storage. It is well suited to the situation where there are many long sets of indices which recieve relatively light use per volume. High tables and stools are used to dis- courage patrons from using this as a study area.

Higher Table Legs
Not Shown

2 x 3 Individual
Desks (Long Legs)

168

Space Saving Principle for Large Tables

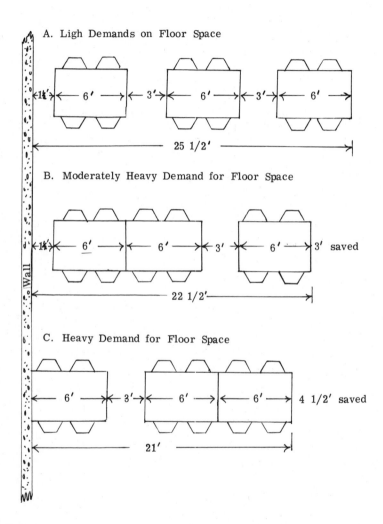

A. Ligh Demands on Floor Space

25 1/2'

B. Moderately Heavy Demand for Floor Space

3' saved

22 1/2'

C. Heavy Demand for Floor Space

4 1/2' saved

21'

Wall

169

The following dimensions have been found to be satisfactory standards for the Undergraduate Library:

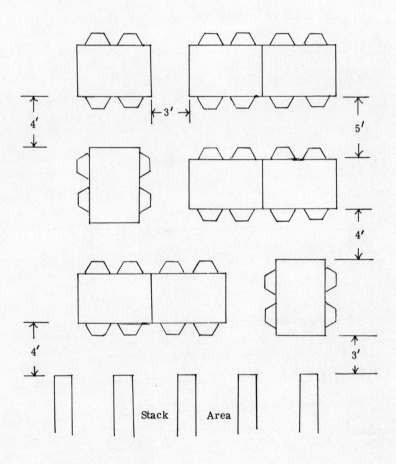

Cost Appraisal of Xerox Copying Service
By: J. J. Cook, M. C. Drott

Purpose:

The purpose of this project is to determine if the present system of Xerox reproduction is economical, profitable, and yields the best possible customer service.

Background:

Xerography was introduced into The University of Michigan Library system during the fiscal year 1961/62. During that year it generated an income of $17,298. Xerographic Service has grown at such a pace that in the fiscal year of 1963/64 it provided the largest single source of income for the Photoduplication Service. In fiscal year 1963/64 the department's model 914 copiers produced 64% of the total income for the department.

Presently, the Xerographic services consist of cash sales, interlibrary loan, credit sales, departmental orders, and University Library system service. The existing system emphasizes $0.10 per copy Xerographic service using 8 1/2" by 11" paper. This system discourages reproduction on large (10" by 14") paper. Reproductions are made on large paper only when the customer specifically requests this size. The reason for discouraging large copy service is that the higher cost of large paper warrants its sale at $0.15 per copy rather than the advertised $0.10.

Consequently, under the present system, approximately 90% of reproductions are made on small (8 1/2" by 11") paper.

Analysis:

Departmental costs for the present system of Xerox reproduction were tabulated and analyzed in the following manner:

1. Costs applicable to Xerox operations were defined. These costs are as follows:

    a. A per copy charge assessed by the Xerox Corporation.

    b. Parts replacement costs for the machines. The primary cost was for replacement of an electrostatic drum with a relatively short useful life span.

  c. Supplies cost consisting of paper and toner, a substance similar to ink.

  d. Miscellaneous costs representing the consolidation of minor costs such as paper clips, staples, other small items and losses due to damaged copies.

  e. Labor costs, wages of people fully or partially assigned to Xerox reproduction.

  f. Machine rental charge, which is a fixed monthly rate for machine use.

  g. Overhead, the cost of supervision, administrative expenses and depreciation of office furnishings.

2. Having defined the costs, data were collected and converted to a common measure of cost per copy output:

  a. The Xerox corporation's assessment is fixed at 3 1/2¢ per copy ($0.035)

  b. Drum replacement occurs on the average of once every 24,000 copies according to annual records kept by the department.

    Converted, this amounts to:

$$\frac{\text{Drum cost}}{\text{Copies produced}} = \frac{\$104.50}{24000} = \$0.0044 \text{ per copy}$$

  c. Supplies costs amounts to:

    (1) Paper:

      (a) 8 1/2" x 11" sheets with a printed copyright notice cost $1.73 per ream (500 sheets)

$$\frac{\text{cost per ream}}{\text{copies produced}} = \frac{\$1.73}{500} = \$0.0034 \text{ per copy}$$

      (b) 10 x 14 sheets with the printed notice

$$\frac{\text{cost per ream}}{\text{copies produced}} = \frac{\$3.69}{500} = \$0.0074 \text{ per copy}$$

The present system produces 90% of the output on small (8 1/2" x 11") paper and 10% on large (10" x 14"). The paper used has a pre-printed copyright notice on the reverse side. The average cost per copy is:

    90% of cost of small paper + 10% of cost of large paper =

$(.90 \times \$0.0034) + (.10 \times \$0.0074) = \$0.0038$

    (2) Toner cost is $7.25 per can when purchased by the the case. Records indicated that over a period of time 40.3 cans of toner produced 29,400 copies. The average yield in copies for one can of toner is:

$$\frac{\text{copies produced}}{\text{toner consumed}} = \frac{29,400 \text{ copies}}{40.3 \text{ cans}} = 730 \text{ copies per can}$$

The cost per copy is:

$$\frac{\text{cost per can of toner}}{\text{average number of copies produced}} = \frac{\$7.25}{730} = \$0.0099 \text{ per copy}$$

d. Miscellaneous costs assignable to Xerox operations amounted to $254 over a six month accounting period. During this time 207,500 Xerox copies had been produced.

$$\frac{\text{misc. costs}}{\text{copies produced}} = \frac{\$254}{207,500} = \$0.0012 \text{ per copy}$$

e. Labor costs were computed as in the earlier report Memo on Effective Labor Cost.

    The amount of time that department personnel spent on Zerox operations was tabulated, the hourly rates applied and average labor expense computed.

Per copy cost for labor was computed by:

$$\frac{\text{average weekly effective payroll (for Xerox operation)}}{\text{average weekly production}}$$

Under present operating conditions this cost amounts to $0.0255 per copy.

f. Machine rental is a fixed cost of $25.00 per machine per month. The present operation uses three machines which average a combined output of 39,000 copies monthly. The per copy cost at present is:

$$\frac{\text{monthly rental expenses}}{\text{average monthly production}} = \frac{\$75.00}{39,000} = \$0.0019 \text{ per copy}$$

    This cost is relatively deterministic. It can be changed only by a change in the number of copiers. One should keep in mind that the per copy figure is based on a specific volume. An alternative would be to treat this cost in the same manner as overhead (g. below).

Analysis of a University Library

    g. Overhead was computed and costs allocated to Xerox operations.

supervisory salary+ secretarial salary + administrative expense + annual write off for depreciation = total overhead
This amounts to $12,947 annually. Records show that 64% of departmental income is contributed by Xerox operations. It is implied that 64% of operating expense can also be allocated to Xerox operations. This amounts to: $12,947 x .64 = $8,286 per year.

This cost is fixed and is independent of the number of copies made (although it is dependent on the total volume of business). It is best to consider this figure as a minimum annual return that must be realized from the operation.

Total Variable Cost Per Copy of Xerox Reproduction

As analyzed, the costs to the Photoduplication Department in producing Xerox copies are:

Direct Materials:

Copy Charge	$0.0350
Parts Replacement	$0.0044
Supplies Expense:	
Paper	$0.0038
Toner	$0.0099
Misc. Costs	$0.0012
Direct Labor	$0.0255
Overhead	
Machine Rental	$0.0019
Supervision and Administration	*
Total Variable Cost Per Copy	$0.0817
Average Selling Price	$0.1050
Margin Per Copy	$0.0233

*to be considered as an annual fixed cost

As can be seen, two major items represent nearly 75% of the

174

expenses to reproduce by Xerox. These items are:

1. Per copy charge assessed by Xerox Corporation 3.50¢
2. Direct labor 2.55¢

Operating Procedures

Work methodology studies were performed to determine if it was possible to make changes which would significantly reduce labor or overhead costs. No significant changes could be made in methods.

Minor costs were studied. Most costs were insensitive to any operational changes. The printing cost for copyright notices was significant and resulted in an additional expense of $600 per year. Rather than being operational, this cost is really an effect of managerial policy.

Demand Sampling

An input-output appraisal was performed in relation to Xerox operations to determine if the present system of operations matched the pattern of demands on the system. The outputs of the system are the two sizes of reproductions sold, i.e., large and small paper sizes of 10" x 14" and 8 1/2" x 11". Input was measured in terms of page size of the material to be copied. Graphically the relationship is represented below.

This appraisal showed that under the present system items with page size A result in production of 2 pages per copy output; items of size B have a resultant production of one page per copy 2 out of 3 times and two pages per copy 1 out of 3 times. Although ideally all copying could be two pages per copy, items of size C have a 1 copy to 1 page ratio. Items of size D have a 1 to 1 ratio but account for less than 1% of total copies produced.

With the accumulated information there is sufficient basis for an economic analysis to determine whether the present system is more economical than other possible systems. The approaches taken for comparative analysis are (A) the extreme opposite from present operations; production with only large paper for output copies, (B) operations with an output appropriate to the ideal output as related to the present demands. Production levels for the varying approaches to operating situation are:

175

Input:

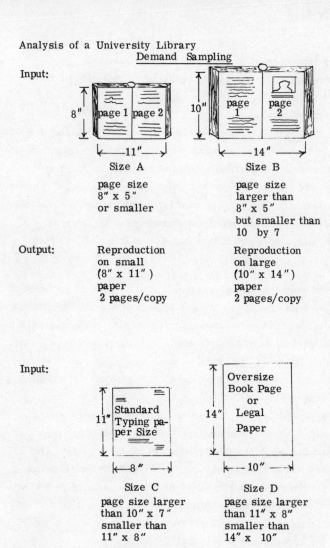

Size A

page size
8" x 5"
or smaller

Size B

page size
larger than
8" x 5"
but smaller than
10 by 7

Output:

Reproduction
on small
(8" x 11")
paper
2 pages/copy

Reproduction
on large
(10" x 14")
paper
2 pages/copy

Input:

Size C

page size larger
than 10" x 7"
smaller than
11" x 8"

Size D

page size larger
than 11" x 8"
smaller than
14" x 10"

Output:

Reproduction
on small paper
1 page/copy

Reproduction
on large paper
1 page/copy

	100 Item Input	Present Output	Situation A	Situation B
Input	Pages per 100*	90% small: 10% large	All large	69% large: 31% small
Size A 30		15 copies	15 copies	15 copies
B 40		33	20	20
C 30		30	30	30
D 0		0	0	0
	totals	78 copies	65 copies	65 copies
	%decrease from present		16.6%	16.6%

*based on a survey of materials received for copying

The difference lies in the extensive use of small paper in the present system. The 40 pages of size B are an input which could be copied on large paper with two pages per copy. But only 1/3 are actually copied in this manner while the other 2/3 are copied on small paper (size C) one page per copy.

Economic Appraisal

Situation A:

This situation supposes that the operations may be run with the total output consisting of large copy reproduction, the opposite extreme from present operations.

Production, as shown in the earlier analysis, will be reduced by 16.6% Toner life which was computed to yield 730 copies per can is estimated at 600 copies per can with the use of solely large paper, as more area must be covered for each copy produced.

The cost-profit evaluation is:

Direct Materials:	
Copy Charge	$0.0350
Parts Replacement	0.0044
Supplies Expense:	
Paper	0.0074
Toner	0.0121
Misc. costs	0.0012
Direct Labor	0.0255
Overhead	
Machine Rental	0.0023
Supervision and Administration	_____*
Total Variable Cost Per Copy	$0.0879

177

Analysis of a University Library

Graphically this is presented as:

Input: A   B   C

Output: Present situation with emphasis on small paper

A   B   C

Situation A with emphasis on large paper.

A   B   C

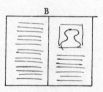

Situation B, copying suitable to page size.

A   B   C

178

Economic Appraisal - continued

Average Selling Price	$0. 1500
Margin Per Copy	$0. 0621

* a fixed cost

The total cost per copy in this situation is higher than present operations but with a fixed sale price of $0. 15 per copy, the profit per copy is increased to almost 3 times the present margin.

In terms of service this system becomes infeasible because there exists a demand for the economy and desirability of small paper reproductions. Although this system appears infeasible in terms of service, the economic analysis indicates that any greater emphasis on large copy reproduction yields a greater profit margin per copy than the present system. The following approach, then, incorporates this consideration.

Situation B

This situation supposes that the operation may be organized to satisfy the demand pattern with an output of 69% small copies and 31% large copies. In accordance with the previous appraisal, production is decreased by 16%.

Only toner cost and paper cost vary compared to Situation A. These become: toner $0. 0106 and paper $0. 0046. The total cost per copy would be $0. 0839 while the average selling price (10¢ x . 69 + 15¢ x . 31) is $0. 1155. The margin for this amounts to $0. 0316.

The annual profit summary indicates the operation should be run according to Situation A for profit maximization. But the study of demand patterns indicates that Situation A is not suitable to satisfy the demand. Moreover, it would be unacceptable to force patrons to accept large copies at 15¢ if most of their material would be more suitably copied on small paper at 10¢. The different situations must be analyzed to determine what effect, in terms of cost, each has on the patron.

Comparative Analysis of the Three Systems

	Present	Situation A	Situation B
Direct Materials:			
Copy Charge	$0. 0350	$0. 0350	$0. 0350

179

Analysis of a University Library

Parts Replacement	0.0044	0.0044	0.0044
Supplies:			
Paper	0.0038	0.0074	0.0046
Toner	0.0099	0.0121	0.0106
Misc. Costs	0.0012	0.0012	0.0012
Direct Labor	0.0255	0.0255	0.0255
Overhead:			
Machine Rental	0.0019	0.0026	0.0026
Supervision & Administration			*
Total Variable Cost Per Copy	$0.0817	$0.0879	$0.0839
Average Selling Price	0.1050	0.150	0.1155
Margin/Copy	$0.0233	$0.0621	$0.0316

* a fixed cost

Annual Profit Summary

	Present	Situation A	Situation B
Annual Production	415,000	345,820	345,820
Direct Materials:			
Copy Charge	$14,525	$12,104	$12,104
Parts Replacement			
Supplies:			
Paper	1,577	2,559	1,590
Toner	4,109	4,184	3,666
Misc. Costs	498	415	415
Direct Labor	10,582	8,818	8,818
Overhead:			
Machine Rental	900	900	900
Supervision & Administration	8,286	8,286	8,286
Total Cost	$40,477	$37,266	$35,779
Total Revenue	43,575	51,873	39,942
Profit	$ 3,098	$14,607	$ 4,163

The following demonstrates the effects of the three situations on the patron. If a person were to have items of size A, B, and C copied by the present system, size B would be copied on two small sheets of paper. Only if it was specifically requested would this size be copied on a large sheet.

Each time a patron has an item of Size B, a savings of $0.05 would be made if the output were on the large paper. Presently 10% of the patrons receive this cost savings which amounts to $0.05 x 41,500 = $2,075 annually. In the ideal system 31% of the output would be made in this manner. The cost savings in this case would amount to $0.05 x 107,216 = $5,360. Thus, in the ideal situation the additional annual savings passed on to the customer amounts to $3,285.

Output: Present situation with emphasis on small paper

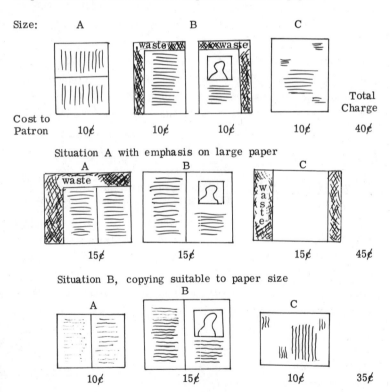

Conclusions

The present system of operations is not the most economical or profitable. It only partially satisfies the demands put upon the system by customers. Production and sale of large reproductions only, as in Situation A, would yield the highest profit to the department. But this system ignores the additional expense to the customers who would be better served by small size copies. Production compatible with the demand pattern, as in Situation B, is most suitable for the best customer service. This system makes better use of labor and reduces the amount paid to the Xerox corporation. The profit of the department would be increased by $1,065 annually. At the same time, patrons would save $3,285 annually. Thus, the authors recommend this system.

The present operation uses three machines. With the output ratio nearly 2:1 (69:31 actual) the system would appear conducive to operating with one machine loaded with large paper while the other two contain small paper. The layout of the department should be changed so that all three machines are fairly close together.

Some patrons may want part of an article copied on large paper and the rest on small. It is recommended that this not be done, because there is an additional labor cost associated with changing machines (estimated to be $0.04).

Additional Studies

1. Study of Undergraduate Library Xerox Operation

The operation in the UGL was found to be different from the General Library operation. The accompanying graphs show that demand and production experience severe fluctuations which create problems unique to this operation. Staffing is one problem; as exam periods approach, two operators and two machines could carry the demand load with a very small lag time between customers. But on certain days throughout the semester, as well as during exam period, demand drops to such a minimum that there is hardly enough work to keep one operator busy.

It was found that one operator, one machine and continuation of the present system of operation is preferable for the UGL. It

182

would prove uneconomical to add another operator and machine. To change the system of operation would be unrealistic because the 90%-10% ratio of the production of small copies to large ones generally suits the demand pattern for these sizes.

Assigning an associated task to the operator during slack periods was also considered during the study. This proved relatively infeasible, because the average free time between customers was 3.45 minutes. Very few tasks could effectively be accomplished in such brief scattered periods.

2. Study of Medical Library Xerox Operation

Xerographic service in the Medical Library was observed and data collected. The distribution of copy sizes in the Medical Library was found to be nearly opposite that of the General Library operation. That is, the Medical Library produces only large copies unless there is a specific request for small (8 1/2″ by 11″) copies. The resultant production approaches 90% copy reproduction on large paper and 10% on small. The Medical Library is able to meet its demand pattern because the majority of its copying is from medical journals which suit 10″ by 14″ paper and exceed the limits of 8 1/2″ by 11″ paper. No major difficulties are encountered in this system of operation and, as has been shown in the "Annual Profit Summary," this system is the most profitable.

3. Objections to the Proposed System

In the early stages of this project an objection was raised that large paper might cause more paper jamming in the Xerox 914, which is used in each of the libraries studied. Observation of the Medical Library, which uses large paper predominantly, did not seem to indicate an increase or decrease in jamming. The Xerox maintenance man stated that no particular difficulties were encountered by using large paper instead of small paper.

Another objection to the system was that 10¢ quick copy service could not be advertised as it can be with the present system. Under the proposed system if a customer has material suitable to large paper, the cost will run less than he may have predicted at 10¢ per page. Should that customer return later with material not suitable to large paper he will have to pay 10¢ per page. This objection is of a psychological nature; the department cannot advertise a clear, concise price per page and the patrons cannot predict the cost of copying unless they can definitely pre-determine which size is most suitable for their material.

An objection to the frequent switching paper in any single machine has been cited earlier in the report.

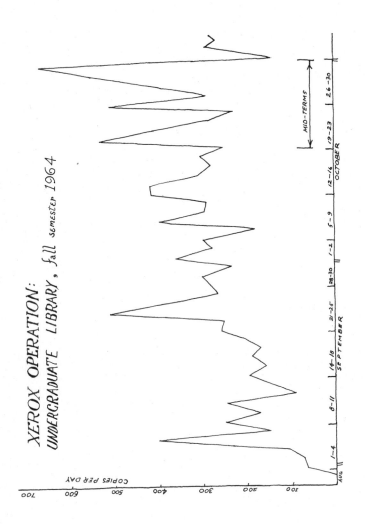

XEROX OPERATION:
UNDERGRADUATE LIBRARY, fall semester 1964

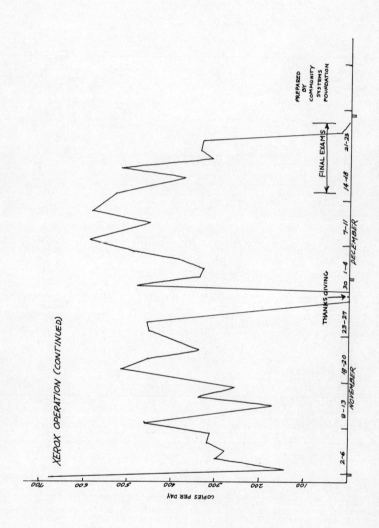